Summary

This report provides guidance on fixings for new cladding systems, that is, for new buildings or overcladding for existing buildings. The following types of cladding systems are covered:

- curtain walling
- precast concrete
- stone
- brickwork/blockwork
- sheet metal.

Rainscreen overcladding is covered under the sections on curtain walling or stone cladding, as appropriate.

Alternative fixings for each system are covered with reference to typical details. Criteria for selection to achieve long service life are discussed.

Practical guidance is provided for the following stages, starting at selection and finishing with in-service conditions:

- design parameters
- installation
- supervision
- testing
- maintenance.

Checklists supplement the above sections for practitioners involved in each stage.

The major publications that are available on this topic are then listed together, providing a means of obtaining more detailed advice.

Acknowledgements

This report is the result of a research project carried out under contract to CIRIA by Taywood Engineering and Harrison Goldman Design Consultants Ltd. It provides good practice guidance on cladding fixings.

The project was developed and managed by Ann Alderson, research manager at CIRIA, with advice and guidance from a project steering group whose support and valuable contributions are gratefully acknowledged. The steering group comprised:

Mr David Curtis (chairman)	Laing Technology Group
Mr Colin Abbott	Stainless Steel Reinforcement
Dr Stephen Cadden	The Rawlplug Co Ltd *representing* *Construction Fixings Association*
Mr Graham Law	Ancon Building Products
Dr David Dulieu	*formerly* Avesta Sheffield Ltd
Mr Keith Fairey	St Martins Property Corporation Ltd
Mr Alistair Gibb	Loughborough University
Mr Steve Green	Cladtech Associates
Mr Phil King	Ove Arup & Partners
Mr Philip Knutsen	Fixing Point Ltd
Dr Stephen Ledbetter	Centre for Window and Cladding Technology
Mr Jack Mindenhall	Halfen Ltd
Mr Mark Salmon	Independent Fixing Consultants
Mr Nick Selves	Glanville Consultants *representing* *Metal Cladding and Roofing Manufacturers Association (MCRMA)*
Mr Roy Thurgood	*formerly* Department of the Environment, Transport and the Regions
Mr Russ Wolstenholme	WS Atkins Consultants.

CIRIA and the author also appreciate the assistance given by the many individuals who were consulted during the project.

The project was funded by:

- Department of the Environment, Transport and the Regions
- Ancon Building Products
- Avesta Sheffield Ltd
- Construction Fixings Association
- Fixing Point Ltd
- Halfen Ltd
- Harrison Goldman Design Consultants Ltd
- Metsec Building Products Ltd
- SFS Stadler Ltd
- Stainless Steel Reinforcement Ltd
- Taywood Engineering.

Contents

Figures

PHOTOGRAPH CREDITS

Figures 3.9 and 3.10 courtesy of Szerelmey Ltd

Figures 6.1, 6.2, 6.7 and 6.9 courtesy of Harrison Goldman Design Consultants

Tables

Abbreviations

BDA	Brick Development Association
CDM	Construction (Design and Management) Regulations 1994
CFA	Construction Fixings Association
CPD	Construction Product Directive
COSHH	The Control of Substances Hazardous to Health Regulations 1994
CWCT	Centre for Window and Cladding Technology
DETR	Department of Environment, Transport and the Regions
EOTA	European Organisation for Technical Approvals – a collective organisation comprising Approved Bodies from each Member State of the EC
ETA	European Technical Approval – methods for demonstrating conformity of products to the essential requirements of the CPD where there are no existing or anticipated Harmonised European Standards
ETAG	Guideline for European Technical Approval
GFRC	glass-fibre-reinforced cement(s); see Glossary
GFRP	glass-fibre-reinforced plastic(s); see Glossary
MCRMA	Metal Cladding and Roofing Manufacturers Association
NAMAS	National Accreditation of Measurement and Sampling
NiDI	Nickel Development Institution
NFRC	National Federation of Roofing Contractors
PTFE	poly tetra fluoro ethylene
SCI	Steel Construction Institute
SCC	stress corrosion cracking

Glossary

With reference to fixings, various terminology is used in different parts of the cladding and fixing industry, with different terms often used to describe the same device (ie fixing, bolt, fastener, anchor etc). Even British Standards vary in their description of terms, depending on the type of cladding. This becomes even more complicated in literature originating outside the UK.

For the purpose of this document and to avoid confusion, it was necessary to define a terminology that could be used consistently throughout the document. Further clarification on different types of fixings can be found in Section 2.2.

anchor	A device used to secure supports or restraints to the concrete or masonry structure, by means of one of the following load transfer mechanisms: mechanical interlock, friction, bond.
angle cleat	A projecting metal angle use to carry load back to the main structure.
bolt	Threaded metal bar with a formed head used with a nut and washer to connect components.
bonded anchor	An anchor which is secured in a hole in the base material by means of either cementitious or polymer-based mortar.
bonding lug	Metal component designed to secure cast-in channels into the concrete.
cast stone	Material cast with aggregate and cementitious binder to resemble natural stone.
cast-in channel (heavy)	Pre-formed channel cast-into structure to receive T-head bolts.
cast-in channel (light)	Pre-formed channel cast-into structure to receive shouldered ties. Also referred to as a dovetail slot (see definition below).
cast-in place	The act of casting a component into concrete.
cast-in socket	Internally threaded metal fixing cast-into concrete to receive a fixing bolt.
cladding	External, vertical or near vertical non-load-bearing covering to a structure.
cladding fixing	Device to support or tie back cladding units.
cladding gasket	Flexible pre-formed extrusion or moulding that provides a seal between part of a structure and its cladding or between adjacent cladding units.
cladding unit	Component of cladding.
cleat	A component projecting from a structure to support cladding.
component	Part of a system that provides load-bearing support or lateral restraint of cladding onto a structure.

composite cladding unit	Cladding unit of more than one material (often with insulating core).
corbel	Cantilevered stone or series of stones of one or more courses that projects to form a bearing.
corbel angle	Crunched support restraint angle.
corbel plate	Metal projecting from backing to provide support for facing slabs (may be a plate let in, or a bent angle), ie a type of cladding fixing.
cramp	Restraint formed from shaped piece of metal suitably bedded into sinkings cut in stone units, to tie them to one another or to their backing.
cross pin	Component part of cast-in socket, which provides anchorage.
dovetail slot	Pre-formed channel cast-into a structure to receive cladding restraint ties; may be one of the following: • traditional – simple dovetail shape, good ultimate capacity but high movement at the working load • proprietary – proprietary shaped dovetail slot providing minimum movement at the working load.
dovetail tie	A masonry tie built into a cast-in dovetail slot and a masonry skin to form a restraint.
dowel	Short piece of material sunk or cast-into adjacent hidden faces to align and/or prevent movement.
edge distance	The distance between the edge of the concrete or masonry structure and the embedded fixing.
expansion anchor	Mechanical anchor that is fitted to a hole in masonry or concrete and secured by the expanding action of shields, cores, sleeves or wedges.
expansion joint	A joint designed to allow components to expand without damaging adjoining components.
facings	External covering of slabs of stone (ashlar); non-load-bearing.
fastener	This is a generic term usually used in sheet metal cladding to refer to, what is for the purpose of this document described as, a screw (see below).
fishtail tie	A masonry tie built into cavity wall construction, where the bond end of the tie is formed by cutting and separating a flat metal plate.
fixing	Device connecting, supporting and/or restraining any two cladding components or a cladding component to the main structure. This is a general term encompassing items such as anchors, bolts, screws etc.
fixing assembly	The assembly consisting of two or more components (anchor, bracket, packing etc) in any combination.
GFRC cladding	Glass-fibre-reinforced cement cladding.
GFRP cladding	Glass-fibre-reinforced plastic cladding.

half-bonded stones	Stone panels with vertical joints half the length of the panel from the next vertical joint above and below.
hand-set stone	Stone panels seated one upon another and supported at defined levels on load-bearing angles or directly to the structure with each stone unit secured with restraint fixings.
liner trays	Shaped internal lining panels that support the insulation in site-assembled, double-skin, profiled sheet metal cladding.
linings	Internal covering of thin slabs of stone; non-load-bearing.
load-bearing cladding fixings	Cladding fixing that transfers the self-weight of one or more cladding units to a structure, in some cases it may also provide some restraint.
locking fixing	Component designed to prevent the fixing assembly becoming loose.
masonry	Construction of stone, bricks or blocks.
masonry tie	A metal tie built into the two skins of a cavity wall.
movement joint (vertical or horizontal)	A joint specifically designed to accommodate movement resulting from the expansion or contraction of the structure or cladding, relative to each other.
rainscreen overcladding	The particular layer of a wall, normally the outermost layer, that prevents the gross passage of rain.
packing	A component of a fixing assembly inserted between the fixture and the head (or washer and nut) of the fixing to enable clamping of the fixture and positional adjustment. Can be grouted in.
plastic anchor	Plastic sleeve that is fitted into a hole in masonry or concrete and secured by an expansion action when a screw is inserted.
post-installed anchor	Anchor usually installed in a drilled hole in concrete/masonry following partial or complete curing of the base material.
powder-actuated fasteners	Fasteners driven into concrete, masonry or steel members by tools using powder-actuated cartridges.
primary fixing	A fixing that crosses the interface between the main structure and cladding. For sheet metal, BS 5427 defines it as the fixing that secures profiled sheeting to the supporting structure.
restraint fixing	A cladding fixing to restrain cladding units against wind load, and/or out of balance effect.
sandwich panel	A panel, formed in the factory, consisting of two parallel profiled metal or concrete sheets separated by, and bonded to, an insulated core. Acts as a composite structural element.
screw	A tapered threaded device for fixing components. Referred to as fastener in sheet metal cladding.
secondary fixing	The fixing that secures the cladding material to components such as brackets and cramps. For sheet metal, BS 5427 defines it slightly differently as the fixing that secures the laps of profiled sheets to each other.

sheeting rail	A structural supporting member connected to the main building structure to transfer loads from the cladding.
shims	Thin pieces of metal or hard plastic used as packing components to correct position of line or level.
sliding restraint fixing	A plate attached to a slab soffit which has metal ties incorporated. The ties are free to move vertically. The fixing provides lateral restraint at the top of a masonry wall.
slotted fixing	A cladding fixing in a slotted hole to allow adjustments.
soft joint	A joint using a filler that can be compressed, and a sealant able to take both tension and compression.
spade bolt	A threaded rod with a flat end (see Figure 3.12).
stack-bonded stones	Stone panels with continuous vertical joints.
stitcher fasteners	Used in profiled metal cladding to join sheets and attach accessories.
stitching rod	A rod (dowel) that is run through holes in brickwork (see Figure 3.11).
support system	A system of components and fixings that provides cladding support.
T-head bolts	Bolts designed to fit into cast-in channels.
threaded stud	A continuously threaded metal rod.
tie	Pre-formed component designed to link cladding to structure.
washer	Usually a circular, flat plate, through which an anchor, bolt or tie bar passes, to allow the load on the head or nut to be spread over a larger area.

1   Introduction

The term "fixings" for cladding denotes the various brackets, cramps, anchors, washers etc that can be used in combination to form a fixing assembly, which attaches cladding to the structure of the building. The cladding may be of stone, brick, precast concrete, metal sheets, curtain walling or rainscreen overcladding, and the structure may be concrete, blockwork/brickwork or steelwork. The fixings are an integral part of the cladding system, and must be considered and designed as such from concept stage.

Cladding fixings are usually hidden, inaccessible and virtually impossible to replace. Their durability and long-term integrity are therefore critical to the continuing safety of the whole cladding system. Poor design and incorrect installation of fixings are among the most frequently cited reasons for failures of cladding systems. Fixings, including those made from stainless steel, are susceptible to one or more of the many forms of corrosion. This can be caused or aggravated by poor design and installation, but equally can be minimised by careful design and selection of the fixings, and correct installation.

Cladding and rainscreen overcladding for existing buildings is increasingly being used for the external envelope of buildings. Modern fixing technology offers a large choice of fixing products in different materials, for an increasingly wide range of applications. To ensure the long-term safety of the fixings and minimise failures, it is therefore essential that all those concerned with the design, selection, installations and maintenance of fixings have a good knowledge and understanding of their performance, compatibility and installation requirements.

The available information is diverse and fragmented. In addition, much of the existing guidance comes from the fixing manufacturers and is neither consistent nor independent. Therefore the objective of this document is to provide all concerned in the design and installation of cladding systems with:

- good practice guidance on the design, selection and specification of fixings, including complete and correct consideration and interpretation of design parameters, good site practice, and provision for inspection and maintenance
- a basic knowledge and understanding of corrosion mechanisms and the design principles to minimise the risk of corrosion.

Where appropriate, the reader is referred to other documents for further guidance.

As part of this project, a questionnaire survey was undertaken to identify answers to the following questions:

- are the current standards and guidance documents providing sufficient information on all aspects of cladding fixings?
- how can the long-term safe functioning of fixings be improved?

The survey targeted all disciplines involved with cladding fixings: manufacturers, structural engineers, architects, contractors etc. It was sent to a total of 231 companies, 26 of which replied. A copy of the questionnaire, as well as the responses, can be found in Appendix B of this report.

The results of the survey can be summarised as follows:

- inadequate on-site supervision of the installation of fixings is one of the most frequent causes leading to failure of the cladding systems
- a simple guidance document which consolidates the available literature is needed to assist in implementing good practice
- the integration of all activities, from an early concept stage to the installation of the fixings and cladding, is essential for their long-term safe functioning.

The guidance given in this document is based on a literature review, consultations with manufacturers, consultants and contractors, and case studies of failures and buildings being demolished.

2   Scope

The document covers new cladding systems, ie for new buildings or overcladding for existing buildings. It does not include guidance on the assessment and repair of existing systems as these are covered in a separate publication: *Appraisal and repair of claddings and fixings* (ICE).

The purpose of this section is to define the types of cladding, fixings and fixings systems considered in this document.

Section 2.1 defines five basic types of cladding, clarifying sub-groups or generic types under each of the cladding systems considered.

Section 2.2 provides broad classification of fixings chosen for the purpose of this document and offers further clarification on different terms used (see Glossary).

2.1   TYPES OF CLADDING

2.1.1   Curtain Walling

Curtain walling is the vertical or near-vertical non-load-bearing external enclosure of the building. In comparison to precast cladding, curtain walling is generally lightweight. The following generic types of curtain wall cladding are considered in this document:

- stick systems – those that are built up from individual mullions and transoms
- unitised – prefabricated units which span vertically from floor to floor
- panelised – prefabricated panels that infill a complete bay, floor to floor and column to column.

Rainscreen overcladding, ie an outer skin of a curtain wall system that sheds water from the building, is also considered in the appropriate sections (eg stone rainscreen over-cladding is covered in the stone cladding section).

Figure 2.1 shows different types of cladding.

2.1.2   Precast concrete

The precast concrete panels considered are non-load-bearing facing panels, self-finished with exposed aggregate or integral factory cast-in finishes, such as natural stone, brick, tiles and mosaics that compose the outer decorative face of the building.

The panels:

- may be storey height, under-sill/spandrel units, mullion units or suspended soffit units
- can be fixed to concrete or steel columns, beams, floors or an *in situ* concrete backing wall
- dead load is transferred back to the structure by cleats, integral nibs and fixings
- may include insulation between two skins of concrete and are then referred to as sandwich panels. (Insulation can also be pre-fixed to the concrete as well as true sandwich panels.)

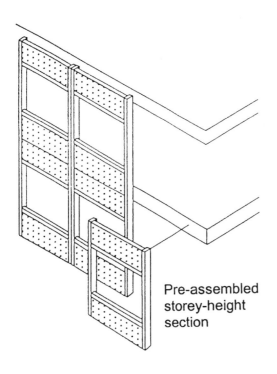

Curtain walling – unitised system

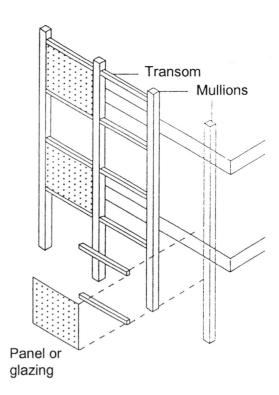

Transom

Mullions

Panel or glazing

Curtain walling – stick system

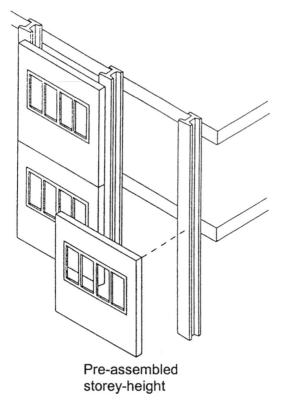

Pre-assembled
storey-height
bay-width panel

Curtain walling – panelised system

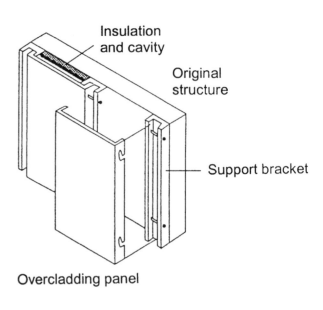

Insulation
and cavity

Original
structure

Support bracket

Overcladding panel

Rainscreen overcladding

Figure 2.1   *Types of cladding* (Centre for Window and Cladding Technology)

2.1.3 Stone

The stone cladding considered is non-load-bearing and may be natural stone or cast stone, as defined in BS 1217. It can be divided into several sub-groups:

- walls that are ashlared (ie faced with stone or cast stone) as the outer leaf of a cavity wall, as defined in BS 5390 but post-fixed
- stone facings mechanically fixed to a structural background and supported at each floor level, as defined in BS 8298
- stone linings mechanically fixed to a structural background and supported at each floor level, as defined in BS 8298
- stone cladding or lining panels individually mechanically fixed on site to a metal or concrete secondary frame, with or without filled joints and commonly referred to as rainscreen cladding
- factory-fitted stone on strongback system.

2.1.4 Brickwork

The brick cladding considered is non-load-bearing cladding that forms the outer decorative face of the building. This includes the following:

- typically a half-brick skin, supported on the structural frame by an angle at each floor level and restrained to the inner leaf with ties
- panels of bricks, supported laterally by windposts, which span vertically from floor to floor
- brickwork cladding on metal decking, where the slab edge trim can incorporate a cast-in channel to provide a fixing for support brackets
- brickwork cladding strengthened by adding joint reinforcement in the horizontal mortar joints.

2.1.5 Sheet metal

Metal cladding is often used to form the outer weathertight skin of a steel-framed building. Four types are considered:

- profiled metal cladding that is fixed on site to sheeting rails. These provide a single sheet of metal as the cladding
- a double skin of profiled sheets with insulation and spacers inserted between, assembled on site
- composite metal panels (sandwich panels) that are fixed on site to sheeting rails. They have an inner and outer profiled sheet skin, with factory-filled insulation between them and act as a composite structural element
- flat composite panels, which may be fixed either to sheeting rails or, in the case of some systems, to secondary metal framing.

Note

No guidance is given in this publication on the use of flat or profiled GFRP or fibre-cement sheets. Roofing is also outside the scope of this document since it has other functional requirements.

2.2 FIXINGS

A cladding fixing is a device that supports or ties back a cladding unit.

A variety of products fall into this category and, as mentioned above, different terms may be used to describe similar products within the building industry. In addition to providing the classification of fixings, this section also provides further clarification on terminology used throughout the document.

Cladding fixings can be classified into three broad categories:

- fixings attached to the structure (primary fixings)
- fixings attached to the cladding (secondary fixings)
- components attaching the cladding to the structure (secondary structure).

Figure 2.2 illustrates the generic parts of cladding systems, as described above.

The "primary fixing" is defined as the fixing that crosses the interface between the structure and component or cladding. For concrete and masonry structures, primary fixings are referred to as anchors. For steel structures, when the cladding is connected directly to the steel component, nuts and bolts are generally used. For composite steel structures, anchors are again used to fix the supports and ties attaching the cladding to the concrete.

A secondary support system or secondary structure (the component attaching the cladding to the structure) is also shown, which could be a lightweight steel beam or a cleat, angle, cramp or bracket. Fixings attaching the cladding to the secondary structure are defined as "secondary fixings".

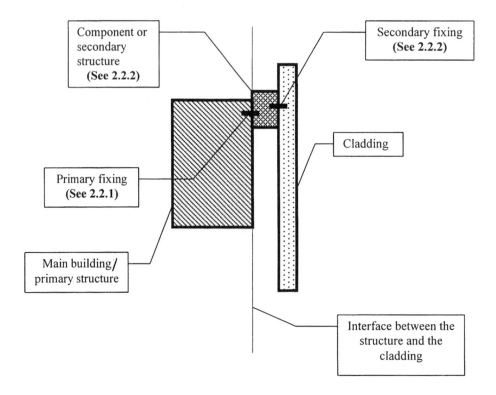

Figure 2.2 *Generic section through the external interface between cladding and structure*

When a secondary structure (ie an angle or a support bracket, see Figure 2.2) is considered in conjunction with a fixing or a number of fixings, it is referred to as a fixing assembly.

There are cladding systems where there is no secondary structure and the primary fixing is the only fixing between the cladding material and the main structure itself.

Fixings are for vertical load-bearing support, horizontal restraint, or combined support and restraint for the cladding unit. Whichever type is used, it is essential to have multiple fixing points rather than rely on a single fixing.

Fixings must be designed to cope with construction tolerances and achieve the line and level specified for the cladding, as well as any differential movement between the cladding and the structure.

It should be noted that **the primary fixing and the secondary fixing are of equal importance**. They have been used in this publication as generic terms for all the cladding systems. The reader should note that BS 5427, which covers the use of profiled metal cladding, also refers to primary and secondary fixings but in a different context (see Sections 1 and 3.2.5).

2.2.1 Fixings attached to the structure (primary fixings)

The purpose of this component is to transfer the external loads to a load-bearing element of the main structure, which can be concrete, masonry or steel. The type of main structure is thus used here as a basis to distinguish different groups of primary fixings.

The broad classification of fixings is provided below. More detailed descriptions of each type, including graphic examples, can be found in Section 3.

Concrete structure (see Section 3.1.1)

- cast-in channel or socket
- post-installed anchors.

Masonry (brickwork and blockwork) structure (see Section 3.1.2)

- plastic anchors
- bonded anchors.

Steel structure (see Section 3.1.3)

- nuts and bolts, when attached directly to the steel
- cast-in channel, socket or post-installed anchor when attached to concrete in the case of a composite structure
- self-drill fasteners (for sheet metal).

2.2.2 Components and secondary fixings attaching the cladding to the structure

Fixings attaching the cladding material to components, such as brackets, are generally referred to as secondary fixings. The fixings used depend on the cladding type.

Below are some examples of the components and secondary fixings used within each cladding system (see Section 3.2 for more details):

- **curtain walling** – support brackets with bolted connections, angle cleats
- **precast concrete cladding** – threaded studs, cast-in channels, cast-in sockets, post-installed anchors, integral concrete nibs, purpose-designed support brackets, angle cleats, heavy-duty cramps
- **stone cladding** – corbels, restraint cramps, restraint dowels, various types of anchors, support brackets, corbel plates, nibs
- **brick cladding** – brickwork support angles/brackets, brick ties, wire restraint fixings, dowel rods
- **sheet metal cladding** – horizontal sheeting rails, liner trays, various types of either self-drilling or self-tapping fasteners for pre-drilled holes.

3   Different types of fixings

This section details the different types of fixings and systems in common use. Installation is covered in Section 6.2.

3.1   PRIMARY FIXINGS

3.1.1   Concrete structure

For concrete structures, the fixings attached to the structure can be divided into two categories:

- post-installed
- cast-in place.

As already mentioned in Section 2.2, these fixings are referred to as anchors.

There are three principal load transfer mechanisms for the above systems:

- mechanical interlock
- bond
- friction.

In case of mechanical interlock, the load transfer is usually concentrated at the end of the component (eg headed or undercut anchor), where high bearing stresses are localised in one region. Bonded components transfer the loads along the embedded length, whilst in the case of a friction mechanism, the direction of the load transfer is perpendicular to the friction surface.

One or more of the above mechanisms can transfer the externally applied loads to the base material.

Most common types of **post-installed anchors** are installed into drilled holes, although some of them can be driven into the base material with impact energy. Expansion and undercut anchors, bonded anchors, plastic anchors and concrete screws are all common types of post-installed anchors.

Figure 3.1 shows examples of the different categories of post-installed anchors used in cladding fixings.

The Comité Euro-International du Beton's publication *Fastenings to concrete and masonry structures* provides detailed information on concrete and masonry anchors.

a) Torque controlled expansion anchors

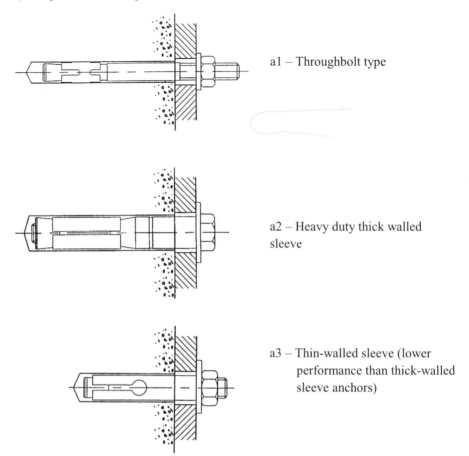

a1 – Throughbolt type

a2 – Heavy duty thick walled sleeve

a3 – Thin-walled sleeve (lower performance than thick-walled sleeve anchors)

b) Deformation controlled expansion anchors

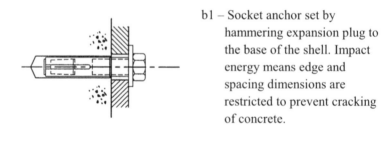

b1 – Socket anchor set by hammering expansion plug to the base of the shell. Impact energy means edge and spacing dimensions are restricted to prevent cracking of concrete.

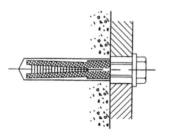

b2 – Socket anchor of brass or stainless steel expanded by insertion of the screw itself. Expansion reduced if screw not fully inserted, therefore extra packing shims will reduce performance. Generally not used to support a total load of 1 kN.

Figure 3.1   *Examples of different types of post-installed anchors (continued overleaf)*

c) Undercut anchors

d) Bonded anchors

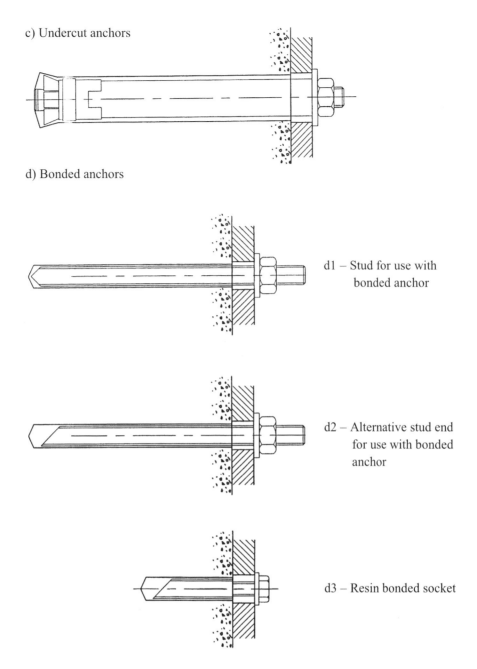

d1 – Stud for use with bonded anchor

d2 – Alternative stud end for use with bonded anchor

d3 – Resin bonded socket

Figure 3.1   *Examples of different types of post-installed anchors (continued)*

Cast-in place anchors are positioned in the formwork before the concrete is cast. Mechanical interlock and/or bond generally transfer the loads.

The most common types of cast-in place anchors are cast-in channels used with T-head bolts and internally threaded sockets used with threaded studs.

In heavily reinforced concrete sections, cast-in systems have an advantage over post-installed anchors since the reinforcement can be designed and placed around the cast-in component to improve load distribution. The extent of this depends on the availability of information on loads during the design process.

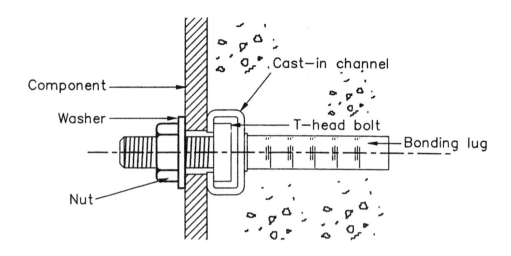

Figure 3.2 *An example of cast-in channel*

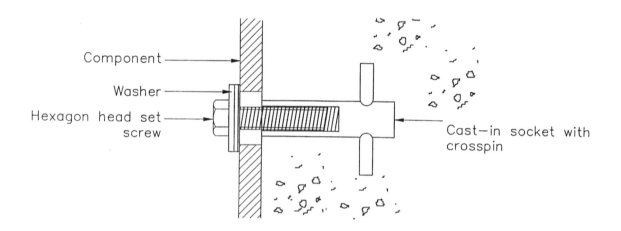

Figure 3.3 *An example of cast-in socket*

3.1.2 Masonry (brickwork or blockwork) structure

Fixings used in masonry structures can be divided into the following groups:

- plastic anchors
- bonded injection anchors.

Plastic anchors (see Figure 3.4) usually consist of a screw and a slotted sleeve, which allows expansion at one end. They are most commonly used in solid masonry with high-strength bricks or blocks.

Anchors have been specially developed for use in both high- and low-strength hollow brickwork and perforated bricks, and in low-strength hollow masonry. Examples are given below.

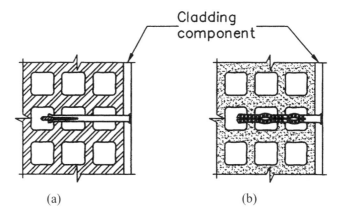

Figure 3.4   *Different types of plastic anchors:*

a) plastic anchor with cone as expansion element for hollow blockwork

b) plastic anchor with screw and long anchoring section for hollow brickwork

Bonded injection anchors (see Figure 3.5) are generally used for masonry materials with a low compressive strength, such as lightweight and aerated concrete, perforated brick or hollow blockwork.

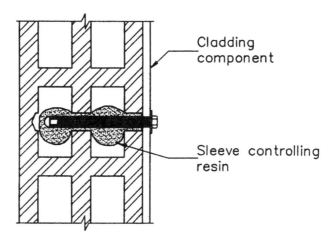

Figure 3.5   *An example of a bonded injection anchor installed in hollow block masonry*

3.1.3 Steel structure

The following details also apply to the use of composite construction floors where *in situ* concrete is added to precast planks or metal decking.

When cladding is attached to multi-storey steel frame buildings, concrete floor slabs are generally utilised, in which case similar fixings as those for concrete structures are used. Direct connections to perimeter steelwork can be made by simple bolts, angles, individually adjustable brackets etc. However, for heavy cladding, slabs with profiled decking are a special case that may require particular attention to fixings. The Steel Construction Institute's *Connections between steel and other materials* (SCI P102) is a useful source of information on this subject. A publication by the Brick Development Association and British Steel, *Brick cladding to steel framed buildings* (BDA DG18), also deals with the connection between the steel frame and masonry cladding.

Steel structures clad in profiled metal sheeting usually have secondary supports in the form of horizontal sheeting rails. The structural steelwork contractor generally fixes these. Other systems, such as composite panels, are fixed directly to the structural steel. Cleats to hold the sheeting rails are typically bolted through the steel column flange, but some systems can be welded on.

3.2 SECONDARY FIXINGS AND COMPONENTS

3.2.1 Secondary fixings and components for curtain walling

In **unitised and panelised systems,** brackets are attached to the structure and set to line and level before the cladding panels arrive on site. This allows panels to be lifted by crane from the delivery lorry and placed onto the brackets on the building, thus preventing double handling and the potential for damage during storage.

For unitised systems the brackets are generally fixed to the edge of the slab or beam. For panelised systems the high loads at the fixing brackets require their location at the columns or beams to be as near the column as possible.

Other unitised and panelised systems usually utilise a proprietary bracket attached to the inside face of the cladding panel. This is then inserted into a mating bracket attached to the structure. In such systems there is no secondary fixing and the cladding panel is prevented from moving by its self-weight. It is important to note that no loads should be carried on slots parallel to the load force.

Stick system curtain walling, built up from mullions and transoms, is usually fixed to the structure by angle cleats that are bolted to each side of the mullions. The mullions will often have vertically slotted holes and the brackets will have horizontally slotted holes. When the mullion has been correctly positioned, an adjacent locking fixing can be used or the position can be fixed by use of serrated surfaces and serrated washers. Note that the direction of serration is perpendicular to direction of load. It is important that a locking fixing used in this system must be correctly designed. If it were to shear under loading, the mullion could move out of position and glazing failures could occur. A typical detail showing serrated washers is shown in Figure 3.6.

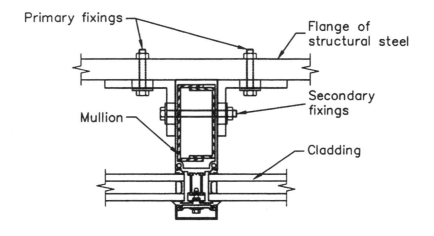

PLAN SECTION

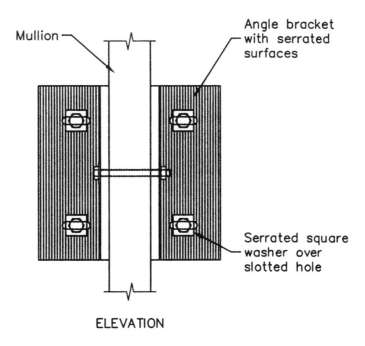

ELEVATION

Figure 3.6   *Curtain walling – a typical fixing detail for stick systems*

3.2.2 Secondary fixings and components for precast concrete cladding

In most cases, the connection is directly between the frame and the panel, by means of brackets and threaded rods. Two types of fixing assemblies are used: load-bearing and restraint. The load-bearing type transfers the dead load vertically into the structure. The restraint type transfers the horizontal loads, such as wind loading and/or out-of-balance effects, from the cladding into the structure. The load-bearing assembly can be at the top of the panel (top-hung) or the bottom (bottom-supported), with the restraint assemblies at both ends. However, BS 8297 cl. 3.2.5.2 states "units should preferably be base-supported (bearing on the lower edge)". This is because a top-hung unit is in continual tension. Any fine flexural cracking caused during early handling will therefore tend to open rather than close, causing greater risk of marking and possibly corrosion of reinforcement. Secondly, it is more difficult to erect top-hung units since a floor slab separates the upper and lower restraints. There are other combinations, for example, when using mullion and spandrel systems.

The panel may incorporate integral concrete load-bearing support nibs, which are positioned over the slab or edge beam and packed with shims to achieve level and line. Most designs position the load over the centre of the edge beam to avoid the effects of torsion. The nibs can incorporate holes or cast-in-sockets for the location of the restraint dowel or cleat. These should be avoided and the full section maintained unless the full concrete cone to resist pull-out can be developed, as shown in Figure 3.8. This will be related to the edge distance restrictions. Where the nibs incorporate projecting reinforce-ment for tying in, it must be accurately located to ensure alignment with the structure.

Panels without nibs will incorporate cast-in-sockets or heavy-duty channels for the attachment of load-bearing angle cleats. Cast-in sockets are often used in pairs for all support conditions but there is a need to ensure that the load is equally distributed between both sockets, each having been designed to take half the load. Depending on the pull-out cone area, single sockets can be more efficient. Horizontal restraint connections are achieved by using either cast-in sockets or heavy-duty channels selected to cope with the differential movement between panel and structure.

They should be able to accommodate imposed loads of both positive and negative impact and overturning. The design should also be able to tolerate the vertical movement that will take place particularly at the upper fixing point of storey-height panels.

Typical fixing details for precast concrete cladding are shown in Figures 3.7 and 3.8.

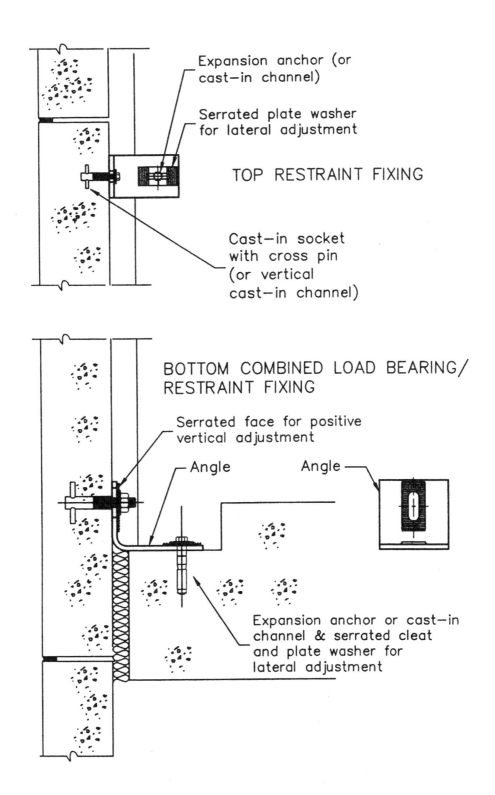

Expansion anchor (or cast—in channel)

Serrated plate washer for lateral adjustment

TOP RESTRAINT FIXING

Cast—in socket with cross pin (or vertical cast—in channel)

BOTTOM COMBINED LOAD BEARING/ RESTRAINT FIXING

Serrated face for positive vertical adjustment

Angle

Angle

Expansion anchor or cast—in channel & serrated cleat and plate washer for lateral adjustment

Figure 3.7   *Precast concrete cladding – bottom-supported panel*

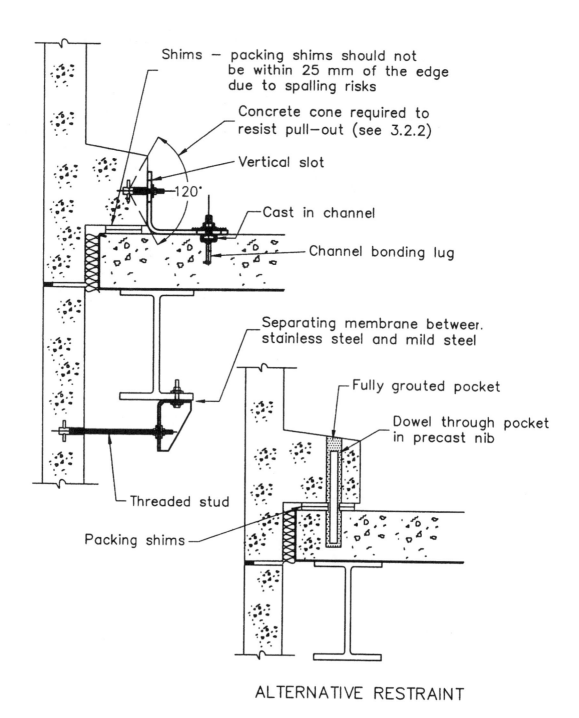

Shims — packing shims should not be within 25 mm of the edge due to spalling risks

Concrete cone required to resist pull—out (see 3.2.2)

Vertical slot

Cast in channel

Channel bonding lug

Separating membrane between stainless steel and mild steel

Fully grouted pocket

Dowel through pocket in precast nib

Threaded stud

Packing shims

ALTERNATIVE RESTRAINT

Figure 3.8   *Precast concrete cladding – bottom-supported panel with a nib*

Figures 3.9 and 3.10 are good examples of how to support large stone-faced precast concrete units.

Figure 3.9 represents an example of the complex fabricated and welded stainless-steel bracket designed to support large stone-faced precast units. The bracket is multi-bolted to the structural steel column and isolated at the contact point of dissimilar metals with isolating plates, washers and tubes. The bolts incorporate locking nuts and have been correctly tightened so the isolating materials are not crushed. Adjustment is achieved using full-face packing shims.

Figure 3.9   *An example of the support for a large stone-faced precast concrete unit*

Figure 3.10 shows an example of stainless steel restraint fixings designed to cope with a large level arm and restrain stone faced precast concrete units. The fixings are designed to provide positive lateral adjustment with a serrated face and full-face packing shims. Isolating plates, washers and tubes are again incorporated at the contact points with the structural steel columns.

Figure 3.10   *An example of stainless-steel restraint fixings*

3.2.3 Secondary fixings and components for stone cladding

All fixings should be designed at an early stage to allow their position to be shown on the stonework details. All mortices for the support angles and cramps can then be formed at the works. This requirement will minimise any damage and subsequent failure of the stone that may occur due to poor or inappropriate working methods.

Hand-set stone will be supported at the movement joint level, which normally coincides with the floor levels. Where this is achieved using angle cleats or corbel plates, they must be provided at two points per stone at the support level. In some circumstances, the stone may be supported directly by the structure. For heavy stonework or where there is a large cavity, the angle corbel may incorporate stiffening gussets.

The angle cleat may have an additional dowel attached to the projecting leg or have the projecting leg inclined upwards at 15°. These types of fixings provide a combined load-bearing and restraint function (see Figure 3.11).

All stones will be restrained with cramps or ties designed to resist positive and negative wind pressure and imposed loads from window cleaning equipment etc. There should be a minimum of two and maximum of four fixing points per stone. To reduce the likelihood of damage to the stone and achieve structural efficiency, the fixings should be located at points one-fifth of the length for stack-bonded stones and one-quarter of the length for half-bonded stones. No fixings should be closer than 75 mm from the corner of the panel.

When using thin stone, where panels are only 20 mm thick, they must be continuously supported on either an angle or the floor slab. Stone panels 30 mm thick or more can be supported on angle cleats or corbel plates.

When required, the cramp may incorporate a drip and insulation retaining facility. However where larger panel sizes and increased wind loads dictate the use of heavy section cramps, the drip feature requires special design considerations with the manufacturer.

Angle cleats, corbel plates, cramps and ties will be attached to the backing structure, using either expansion anchors, bonded injection anchors or cast-in channels. The selection will be based on the individual performance figures, imposed loads and type of backing structure.

When stone is used as lining, the method of fixing will be similar to that used for hand-set stone cladding. The design of the fixings will take into account the different loading actions that exist when all the loads are generally lower.

When stone is used for **rainscreen cladding,** each panel will be individually supported and restrained. The lower fixings will provide a combined support/restraint facility whilst the upper fixings are for restraint only.

For both hand set stone and rainscreen cladding, when adjacent panels share a combined support/restraint fixing, the dowel crossing the joint must also accept the small differential movement. This is achieved by the use of a plastic sleeve set into the panel edge, which allows the dowel to slide. When using this type of fixing, the holes to receive the dowel and sleeve must align across the joint and be pre-drilled at works. These fixings tend to be part of a standard system and can be bolted or grouted into the backing structure (see Figure 3.12).

For some types of rainscreen cladding, the stones will incorporate undercut anchor fixings preset in the rear face of the stone. These fixings are used with other fixing components to provide a combined support/restraint fixing. The Centre for Window and Cladding Technology's publication, *Performance and testing of fixings for thin stone cladding*, provides extensive information on this subject.

Typical fixing details for stone cladding are shown in Figure 3.11 and 3.12.

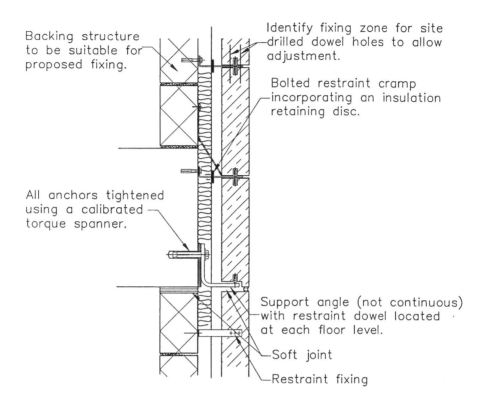

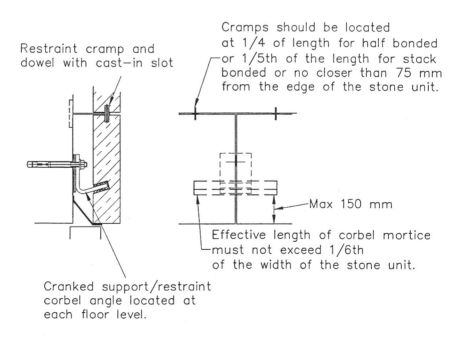

Figure 3.11   *Hand-set stone cladding*

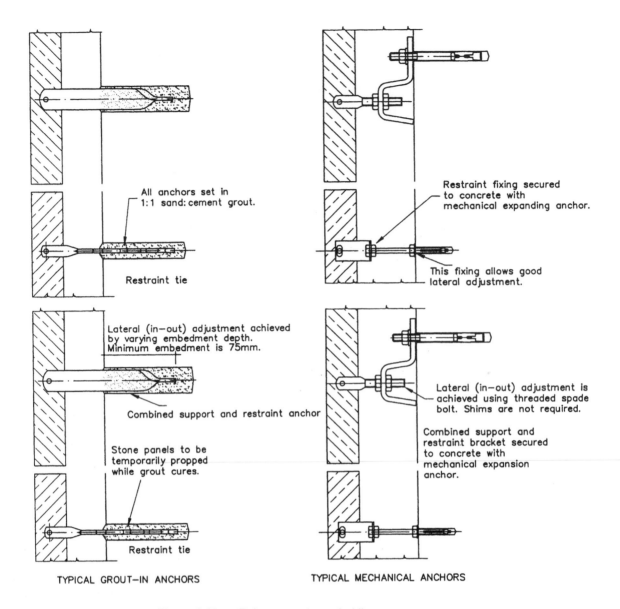

All anchors set in
1:1 sand:cement grout.

Restraint tie

Restraint fixing secured
to concrete with
mechanical expanding anchor.

This fixing allows good
lateral adjustment.

Lateral (in–out) adjustment achieved
by varying embedment depth.
Minimum embedment is 75mm.

Combined support and restraint anchor

Stone panels to be
temporarily propped
while grout cures.

Restraint tie

Lateral (in–out) adjustment is
achieved using threaded spade
bolt. Shims are not required.

Combined support and
restraint bracket secured
to concrete with
mechanical expansion
anchor.

TYPICAL GROUT–IN ANCHORS

TYPICAL MECHANICAL ANCHORS

Figure 3.12   *Rainscreen stone cladding*

3.2.4   Secondary fixings and components for brick cladding

Brickwork may be supported at each floor level on a purpose-made shelf angle or
proprietary bracket bolted to the slab or edge beam. Alternatively, but less frequently,
brickwork is supported at each floor on structural toes projecting from the edge beam.

Both shelf angles and proprietary support brackets are purpose-designed to suit
each situation. The proprietary systems use standard components where possible. All
support methods should be designed so that the deflection at the toe of the bracket or
angle is limited to 1–1.5 mm at the working load when the heel is properly packed
(see Figure 6.8).

Whatever method of support is selected, it must provide support to a minimum two-
thirds of the depth of the brick above. The support method should be designed to cope
with the specified structural tolerances, taking note of the maximum packing
requirements for the method of bolting selected. It is essential to have a horizontal
movement joint below the support level, and a sliding restraint fixing.

Brick cladding is restrained with ties located at the positions specified in the appropriate British Standards (BS 1243:1978, BS 5628: Parts 1 and 3: 1985 and DD140: Part 2: 1987).

The type of cramp or tie is dependent on the method of construction and backing structure. If the backing wall is raised at the same time, a standard masonry tie can be used. If the outer skin is built separately, the following options are available: cramp-fixed with bolt or screw, cramp in cast-in channel or dovetailed slot, cramp in surface-fixed channel. These ties are supplied as standard but their projection length can be adjusted to suit individual contract requirements. At the horizontal movement joint below the support system, sliding ties may be required to restrain the brickwork below while allowing movement. At vertical movement joints, at the edge of each panel, smooth sleeved ties may be required across the joints. Under no circumstances should fishtail ties be used because, when built into an inner leaf, the sharp corners present a safety hazard until the outer leaf is built.

In brick cladding, experience has shown that the mass of the brickwork and normal cavity wall ties in the brickwork above is sufficient to provide restraint. The wall ties are positioned at 450 mm centres within 300 mm above the support angle. The bricks are laid in the conventional manner using support angles fixed to the slab edges or edge beams. Where the architect does not want to see the soffit of a support angle, brackets are available with metal restraint loops that tie into the vertical joints. A positive connection can be obtained by threading reinforcement rods through the pre-formed holes in the bricks and the wire loops (see Figure 3.13). Sometimes a rebated brick (often wrongly called pistol bricks) conceals the edge of the shelf angle. This also allows a horizontal compression joint to be designed in the brickwork of a size compatible with the brickwork bed joints. The brickwork below the support is restrained by a sliding restraint fixing (see Figure 3.14).

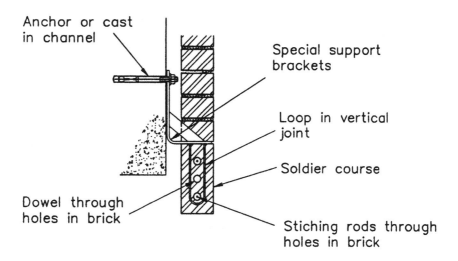

Figure 3.13   *Concealed brickwork soffit detail*

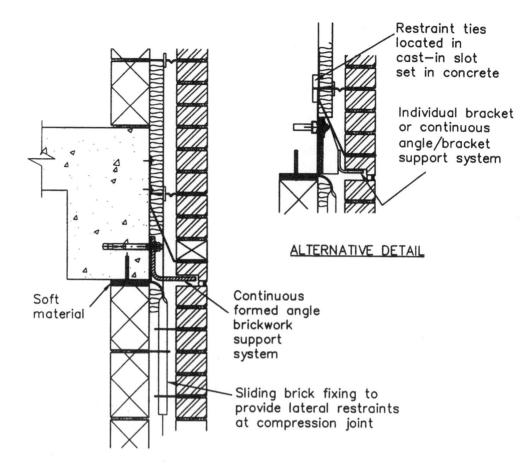

Restraint ties
located in
cast—in slot
set in concrete

Individual bracket
or continuous
angle/bracket
support system

ALTERNATIVE DETAIL

Soft
material

Continuous
formed angle
brickwork
support
system

Sliding brick fixing to
provide lateral restraints
at compression joint

Figure 3.14 *Brickwork cladding – typical detail for continuous angle support system*

3.2.5 Fixings and components for sheet metal cladding

Profiled metal and insulated composite panels (sandwich panels) are normally fixed to cold-rolled sheeting rails that are supported on the structural frame by bolts and brackets. Sheeting rails do not form part of the wall cladding contract and are normally installed with the structural frame. Although in the context of this book the sheeting rails may be considered as secondary components, this is not a term that would be recognised by sheet metal cladding installers.

Fixing between profiled metal cladding and sheeting rails is normally made with self-drilling screws and appropriate sealing washers. Self-tapping screws may be used with pre-drilled holes especially into thicker hot-rolled steel.

Uninsulated constructions using single-skin metal sheet are normally fixed directly to the sheeting rails. Other buildings incorporate insulation between two sheets of metal cladding. These may be built up on site or may be supplied by the manufacturer as a pre-formed composite panel. Site-assembled insulated systems use liner sheets directly fixed to the sheeting rails. Spacer systems are fixed through the liner sheet to the sheeting rails. The insulation and outer weather sheet are then fixed to the spacer.

Insulated prefabricated composite panels are normally fixed to the sheeting rails with sheet support fasteners. In addition to the normal thread to hold the sheeting rail, they have a second thread below the head. This thread holds the outer skin of the composite against the sealing washer to form a weathertight seal with minimal risk of compression of the insulation. The outer skin of the composite panel will be typically in the thickness range 0.4–0.7 mm, which necessitates the use of a different thread form to that of the main thread which fixes into the thicker sheeting rails. The specifier should therefore follow the composite panel manufacturer's recommendation in selecting these specialised fasteners.

Some flat composite panel systems do not use sheeting rails and the panels are fixed to a grid of subframes. There are other systems that use liner trays, which replace the internal metal sheet and obviate the need for sheeting rails. The trays are C-shaped metal sections that span either between the columns or vertically between floor to eaves beam and also support the insulation.

The side-laps of most types of metal sheeting need to be connected by stitching fasteners, which are typically self-drilling screws. These screws not only have to hold two thin metal sheets (typically 0.5 mm thick) together; they often have to compress a seal within the side-lap. The thread form of most stitcher screws is therefore different from that of equivalent length screws that are used to attach sheets to the supports.

There are a number of fixings involved in these systems, as shown in Figure 3.15. The references on sheet metal listed in Section 4 give extensive coverage to the range of fixings available.

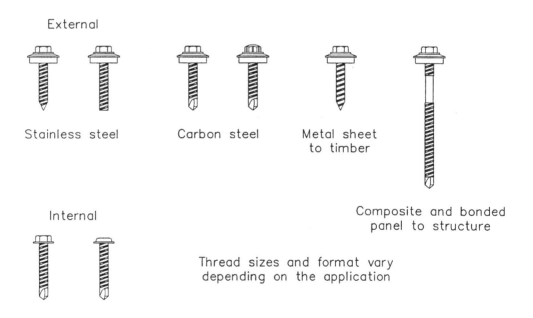

Figure 3.15   *Self-drill, self-tapping fasteners*

Washers are important in all the cladding fixings but in sheet metal cladding they provide the watertight seal to the building. An EPDM vulcanised bonded washer or an EPDM ring is used to seal the interface between the fastener and the outer sheet face. In all cases, the fasteners need to be installed in accordance with the manufacturer's recommendations supplied with the fasteners to avoid over-tightening and deformation of the seal.

The specifier should always refer to the supplier of the metal cladding system for fixing recommendations. A typical profiled sheet metal site-assembled cladding detail, with built-up insulated panels is shown in Figure 3.16.

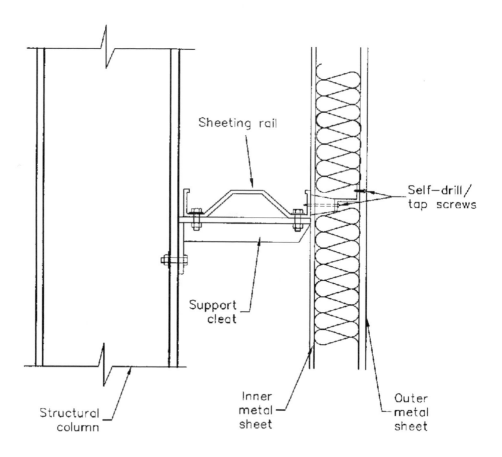

Figure 3.16   *Sheet metal site-assembled insulated cladding*

3.3 MATERIALS FOR FIXINGS

The selection of materials for a fixing is undertaken by the fixing manufacturer, who underwrites the performance of the product by using the correct design, materials specification and manufacturing methods. However, almost all the materials used in fixings are themselves covered by standard specifications, as are many manufactured components.

This section describes in outline some relevant standards for steel products used in the fixings industry. Other materials used for fixings, ie copper and aluminium, are not covered by any British Standard in the same way. It is therefore recommended that further information on copper and aluminium properties be obtained from the Copper Development Association and the Aluminium Federation (contact details can be found in Sources of information.)

An outline knowledge of the steel specifications listed below is of value, both in checking suppliers' product specifications and when considering special fixing requirements where it may be necessary to use a non-standard item.

Any non-standard fixing should have the materials fully specified to the latest relevant standard. Terms such as "mild steel", "galvanised" and "carbon" or "stainless" steel should be avoided. The standards listed give the minimum specified mechanical properties of materials. These can be used for design purposes although, in many austenitic stainless-steel products, actual properties levels in finished components will be higher because of work hardening effects.

Structural steels

Larger fixing items may incorporate components made from hot-rolled sections, plates and bars. In most cases these will be to the same strength/toughness requirements as conventional structural steelwork. The relevant standards for specifying the steels are:

BS EN 10025:1993   *Hot rolled products of non-alloy structural steels, technical delivery conditions.*

Lighter-gauge flat and cold-formed products may use materials drawn from:

BS 1449:1991   *Steel plate, sheet and strip, parts 1.2 and 1.5.*

Reinforcing bars

In addition to being used as reinforcement, ribbed bars may be used as components of fixing systems. The relevant standards are:

BS 4449: 1997   *Specification for carbon steel bars for the reinforcement of concrete* (see also DDENV 10080)

BS 6744: 1986   *Specification for austenitic stainless steel bars for the reinforcement of concrete* (undergoing revision).
For reinforcing bars made of steel type '304' (alloy grade 304S31), BS EN 10088 designation is 1.4301 while for '316' (alloy grade 316S33), BS EN 10088 designation is 1.4436.

Engineering steels

Engineering steels are carbon and alloy steels, used in a range of sizes and strength levels for load-bearing components such as dowels and other machined and threaded components. The major UK specification is:

BS 970   *Specification for wrought steels for mechanical and allied engineering purposes*

          – Part 1: 1996   *General inspection and testing procedures and specific requirements for carbon, carbon-manganese, alloy and stainless steels* (but only for stainless steel in the form of forgings).

Fasteners

(Note: fasteners, as referred to in the standards below, also include anchors. The rest of this document defines fasteners as screws.)

Steels for cold-forged fasteners and similar components are specified in BS 3111 as:

BS 3111   – Part 1:1987   *Specification for carbon and low alloy steel wire*
            – Part 2:1979   *Stainless steel* (includes seven steel grades, including the austenitic steels 304S17 and 316S17).

The mechanical properties of fasteners are specified in:

BS EN 20898 – Part 1:1992 *Bolts, screws and studs.*

This covers products up to 39 mm in diameter with any triangular ISO thread and made of carbon or alloy steel.

Stainless-steel bolts, screws, studs and nuts up to 39 mm diameter with defined chemical compositions and mechanical properties are specified in:

BS EN ISO 3506–1:1998   *Mechanical properties of corrosion-resistant stainless steel fasteners.*

It is possible to obtain studding in classes 50, 70, 80, but these are not commonly used. Since studding cannot be identified except through testing, it is necessary to limit design stresses to the lowest value (50) for unverified material, even when specified as class 70.

Fasteners are also available as bi-metal screws. As the name suggests, the fastener is manufactured from two materials, carbon-steel drill point lead on threads and a stainless-steel body and head.

Stainless steel

It is estimated that more than 90 per cent of fixings used in cladding are made of stainless steel. The section on stainless steel below is therefore covered in more detail than the other metals.

Stainless steels form a large group of materials based on alloying iron with at least 10.5 per cent chromium. Ranges of both mechanical properties and corrosion resistance can be achieved, depending upon chemical composition and treatment.

It is usual to subdivide the stainless steels into four major groups by type of microstructure:

* austenitic
* ferritic
* martensitic
* duplex stainless steel.

Physical characteristics, such as thermal expansion and conductivity, differ between these groups.

These steels are fully described in the three parts of the standard BS EN 10088: 1995.

BS EN10088 – 1:1995   *List of stainless steels*

– 2:1995   *Technical delivery conditions for sheet/plate and strip for general purposes*
(this part officially replaced BS 1449; Part 2: 1983(1991) for stainless-steel chemistry in 1995.)

– 3:1995   *Technical delivery conditions for semi-finished products, bars, rods and sections for general purposes*
(this part officially replaced BS 970; Part 1: 1991 for rolled products in 1995).

Although most stainless-steel fixings are made of austenitic grades, the standard includes a range of steels with higher strengths (duplex and martensitic) and enhanced corrosion resistance (duplex and high alloy austenitic steels) for special applications. The most widely used steels for fixings, however, are the austenitic 1.4301 and 1.4401 grades in this standard.

These grade designations are based on the German DIN system. The steels are widely known by the designations of the closely similar grades 304 and 316 in BS 970: Part 1:1991 (replaced for stainless-steel rolled products by BS EN 10088 Part 3) and grade 304S31 and 316S31 in BS 1449, Part 2:1983(1991) (replaced by BS EN 10088 Part 2).

The chemical compositions of these austenitic steels are given in Table 3.1, from which it is seen that 1.4301 is nominally an 18 per cent chromium, 9 per cent nickel steel, 1.4401 has an addition of 2 per cent molybdenum and a higher nickel level of around 11 per cent. These additions improve the corrosion resistance, but make the steel more expensive. The physical properties and proof strength values for the two steels are given in Table 3.2.

Table 3.1   *Chemical composition of austenitic steel (from BS EN 10088-3)*

This table only applies to rod and bar. For sheet, plate and strip, BS EN 10088-2 applies. This gives different (higher) values for proof stress.

	1.4301 (304S31) (A2)	1.4401 (316S31) (A4)
Carbon max	0.07	0.07
Silicon max	1.00	1.00
Manganese max	2.00	2.00
Sulphur max	0.030	0.030
Chromium min/max	17.00/19.50	16.50/18.50
Nickel min/max	8.00/10.50	10.00/13.00
Molybdenum min/max	–	2.00/2.50
Phosphorus max	0.045	0.045
Nitrogen min/max	0.11 max	0.11 max

Table 3.2   *Physical and mechanical properties of stainless steel (from BS EN 10088-1 and 3)*

	1.4301 (304S31)		1.4401 (316S31)
Modulus of elasticity at 20°C (kN/mm²)	200	200	
Density (kN/mm³)	7900		8000
Mean coefficient of thermal expansion between 20°C and 100°C) (10^{-6}/°C)	16.0	16.0	
Proof stress $R_{p0.2}$min (N/mm²) (in the softened condition)	190	200	

BS EN 10088 also includes a range of stainless steels of higher strength and of higher corrosion resistance than the standard "300" series for special circumstances.

Proprietary stainless steels that offer other solutions for fixing applications are available.

4 Current guidance

The results of the survey carried out at the onset of this project suggested that good practice could be improved by regularly updated reference documents and the provision of guidance on frequently needed information. Numerous publications are available that provide guidance on cladding fixings, ranging from documents produced by national institutes and associations, to those from individual manufacturers. The number and diverse range of their sources make it difficult for the designer and specifier to identify the appropriate information easily, however, while some publications cover only one aspect of the fixings performance, such as corrosion, tolerances or torque.

The listing below attempts to group those major publications that are good sources of frequently needed information. In addition, various manufacturers issue publications providing guidance on the use of their own products, but they are too numerous to be listed here.

- Brick Development Association and British Steel Corporation, DG18: *Brick cladding to steel framed buildings*
  Guidance for architects, engineers and technicians with illustrations of modern practice combining steel frames and brickwork cladding in non-domestic buildings.

- BRE, Digest 235: *Fixings for non-load-bearing precast concrete cladding panels*
  Gives guidance on the factors to be considered in the design and use of fixings.

- BSI, BS 1217: 1997: *Specification for cast stone*
  Gives guidance on the use of cast stone.

- BSI, BS 5080: *Structural fixings in concrete and masonry*
  Part 1: 1993 – Method of test for tensile loading
  Part 2: 1986 – Method for determination of resistance to loading in shear
  Test methods for fixings installed in solid materials.

- BSI, BS 5427: Part 1: 1996: *Code of practice for the use of profiled sheet for roof and wall cladding on buildings*
  Gives recommendations for fixings for external walls that use profiled sheeting.

- BSI, BS 5628:Part 3: 1985: *Use of masonry: Materials and components, design and workmanship*
  Basic guidance on suitable materials and typical details for components associated with masonry support or lateral restraint.

- BSI, BS 7543: 1992: *Guide to durability of buildings and building elements, products and components*
  Gives guidance on durability, required and predicted service life and design life of buildings and their components and/or parts.

- BSI, BS 8297: 1995: *Code of practice for design and installation of non-load-bearing precast concrete cladding*
  Gives recommendations for non-load-bearing units fixed to structural frames or walls and units used in part or whole as permanent formwork.

- BSI, BS 8298: 1994: *Code of practice for design and installation of natural stone cladding and lining*
  Gives recommendations for mechanically fixed facing units held to a structural background by metal fixings or as stone faced precast concrete units.

- BSI, BS EN 10088: *Stainless steels*
  The European Standard for specifying stainless steel.

- BSI, DD140: Part 2: 1987: *Recommendations for design of wall ties*
  Design of wall ties, including remedial ties, used in masonry and timber frame construction.

- British Steel: *Roofing and cladding in steel – a guide to architectural practice*
  Clear guidance on typical fixings and components for sheet metal cladding.

- CEB, Comité Euro-International du Beton: *Design of fastenings in concrete*
  A state-of-the-art report for the design of fastenings in concrete based on the safety concept of partial safety factors. It covers all loading directions and failure modes for expansion, undercut and headed anchors. It is applicable to new construction and the repair and strengthening of existing structures.

- CEB, Comité Euro-International du Beton: *Fastenings to concrete and masonry structures*
  This report presents the behaviour of fixings in concrete and masonry for a range of loading types, ie monotonic, sustained, fatigue, seismic and impact. It also discusses the influence of environmental effects, based on experimental results from various parts of the world.

- CEB, Comité Euro-International du Beton: *Fastenings for seismic retrofitting*
  A state-of-the-art report describing the design concepts and methods for seismic retrofitting with emphasis on the use of fastening systems based on worldwide data.

- CFA Guidance Notes under the following titles:
  Anchor selection
  Anchor installation
  Procedure for site testing construction fixings
  Bonded anchors
  Heavy duty expansion anchors
  Fixings for brickwork and blockwork
  Fixings and fire
  European technical approvals for construction fixings
  Undercut anchors

- CIRIA, Technical Note 136: *Fixings in cracked concrete: the probability of coincident occurrence and likely crack width*
  This document offers basic guidance on the performance of fixings in cracked concrete, a frequently raised issue as concrete cracks even in compression areas and fixings will attract cracks due to the concentration of stresses.

- CIRIA, Technical Note 137: *Selection and use of fixings in concrete and masonry: interim update to CIRIA Guide 4*
  This document contains simple and basic information relevant to the types of fixings used in concrete and masonry as base material.

- CIRIA, Special Publication 87: *Wall technology: Volumes A–G*
  These volumes provide clear, concise guidance on the theory and practice of external wall construction.

- CWCT: *Performance and testing of fixings for thin stone cladding*
  Natural stone cladding units are becoming thinner. BS 8298 covers the more traditional thicker stone units, while this report discusses different methods of fixing thin stone cladding units and the tests to ensure satisfactory performance. It also gives advice on the selection of materials, bimetallic corrosion, staining, etc.

- CWCT: *Guide to the selection and testing of stone panels for external use*
  This document addresses the issues regarding natural stone as an external cladding material and provides guidance to ensure that the selected stone meets the required aesthetics, durability and strength requirements.

- The Institution of Structural Engineers: *Aspects of Cladding*
  Advises on fixing design and selection, basic corrosion and the load cases that must be considered.

- Metal Cladding and Roofing Manufacturers Association
  Provides a number of guidance documents on sheet metal cladding.

- Nickel Development Institute (NiDI), Publication 12010: *Stainless steel in swimming pool buildings*
  The document gives practical advice on the successful use of stainless steel in swimming pool buildings

- The National Federation of Roofing Contractors: *Profiled sheet metal roofing and cladding, a guide to good practice*
  Describes current good practice in the use, application and methods of construction of profiled metal sheeting.

- The Steel Construction Institute: *Architects guide to stainless steel*
  General guidance on stainless steel architectural components.

- The Steel Construction Institute: *Curtain wall connections to steel frames*
  Advises on the efficient design and erection of these connections and appraises six generic cladding systems in relation to the optimised practice.

- The Steel Construction Institute: *Design of stainless steel fixings and ancillary components*
  Guidance on the safe and efficient use of stainless-steel fixings and components.

- The Steel Construction Institute: *Connections between steel and other materials*
  Examines the design and construction issues related to these connections and presents a range of details.

- The Steel Construction Institute, SCI-P-157: *Stainless steel angles for masonry support*

- The Steel Construction Institute, SCI-P-123: *Concise guide to the structural design of stainless steel.*

5 Long-term safe functioning of fixings and fixing systems

In the majority of cases, fixings and fixing systems perform well for the full length of their design life. Careful planning and selection, as well as consideration of fixings not as an isolated unit but as an integral part of the cladding system, can usually prevent premature failure. This section explains the principles to be followed to avoid failures.

5.1 TYPICAL CAUSES OF FAILURE

The typical causes of failure, which are listed below, can easily be avoided if good design and installation practice is followed.

5.1.1 How to avoid fixing failures

A fixing or fixing system fails when it does not provide the support and/or restraint that the application requires. The failure condition may be built in from the design stage, arise through actions during construction or occur during the life of the building itself.

It is claimed that 80 per cent of failures are due to the following causes:

- location
- oversized holes
- fixings overloaded: loss of load capability over time.

Some causes of failure are generic. For example, a lack of information on and training in the properties and use of fixings can affect activities across the phases of design, specification and installation. Lack of information on settlement and other site-specific factors can influence subsequent service performance.

Successful fixings practice requires that the appropriate information is available to all involved and that there is a free flow of this information between all parties, from fixings manufacturers to those responsible for building maintenance and modification. One of the major findings of the questionnaire survey indicated the importance of integrating all activities for successful cladding installation, from early conception to installation.

The five principal classes of failure are discussed below.

Design failures

Design failures result from the specification of a number or type of fixings, which are either inadequate for the load conditions, or are of a type which cannot be installed correctly within the construction process. Whilst anchors from different manufacturers may be the same generically, this does not ensure that the anchor will function properly or achieve required performance. Specifiers should satisfy themselves that the anchor meets the required criteria.

Location failures

These result from wrong location and/or poor preparation of holes. The implication of this type of failure is that adequately designed systems and correctly specified fixings cannot achieve their full performance.

Installation and tolerance problems leading to failure

Typically the fixing may be over-stressed by the installer attempting to overcome tolerance problems. These are most often due to inaccurate structural frame positioning, inaccuracies in the manufacture of the cladding or inappropriate selection of tolerances between the cladding and the frame.

Fixing component failures

Fixing component failures, such as bending, pull-out or even fracture, result from exceeding load-bearing capacity. This may occur, for example, because some fixings have been damaged on installation or omitted, or because forces or moments have been increased by misalignment or excessive use of packing.

In-service failure

In-service failure occurs where fixings fail or have their load-bearing capacity reduced by in-service conditions. Avoidance of corrosion is an essential part of the initial specification of fixings and is discussed further in Section 5.2. Disturbance to fixings by settlement, wind forces or other loading requires consideration at the design stage. Disturbance during maintenance and refurbishment can be covered by providing appropriate guidance information.

Successful, safe functioning of fixings is controlled by the interdependence of good design, good installation practice and adequate site control and inspection.

Design and planning

At the design and planning stage, the numerical and geometrical calculations must be backed by an assessment of the buildability of the project, bearing in mind that fixings are an integral part of the cladding system and cannot therefore be considered in isolation. This will include issues such as:

- how can the fixings installation and tolerance requirements be achieved within the proposed construction programme?
- if changes in the construction programme, or non-availability of cladding elements at the required time, alter the erection sequence, will this require the selection of fixings and sequence of assembly to be reassessed?
- is the variety of sizes and types of fitting specified capable of rationalisation, to minimise the risk of errors (eg fixings being used at wrong locations, or the wrong combinations of components etc)
- are the drawings and specifications comprehensive enough to ensure that there is no ambiguity in the ordering of fixings and making preparations for installation?
- can the fixings and the cladding be installed, replaced and removed in a method that is safe?

Installation

At the installation stage the primary requirements are for adequate training and briefing of installers and effective quality control operations. Critical questions include:

- are the installers and fixers fully instructed in the procedures to be used on the project (which must include a safety induction course)? Are they provided with the necessary equipment (drills of the correct size, torque spanners etc) and trained in its use?

- is the control of the issue of fixings and equipment sufficient to minimise the risks of confusion between different fixings and the non-availability, at the point of installation, of the correct washers, spacers, resin, components, etc?

- are fixers trained to identify potential problem areas, such as cast-in channels and slots cast in the wrong locations?

- are fixers aware of their limits of responsibility and when to seek authorisation for actions, such as modification of packing, locations of holes or adjustments to cope with misalignments?

- are fixers aware of unacceptable practices, such as failing to allow movement at expansion joints, using home-made fixings or mixing of metals giving risk of galvanic corrosion? Anchors must not be modified to suit the site conditions without a design check

- what inspection procedures are in place to monitor standards and are the workforce aware of the importance, for example, of anchor tests to ensure that performance is maintained?

- are installers fully aware of how to check the accuracy of the structural frame to identify potential problems before installation starts?

- are supervisors checking the effective embedment depth of anchors?

Appendix A supplies a number of checklists specifically designed for all those involved: designers/specifiers, supervisors/foremen, installers etc.

5.1.2   Examples of common failures

This section identifies typical causes of failure. They have been grouped as manufacturer, designer and installation issues.

It should be noted that corrosion has been deliberately omitted from this section because of its inherent complexity. It is covered separately in Section 5.2.

Manufacturer issues

- The performance and limitations of fixings when used with load-bearing angles should be provided by manufacturers. The fixing should not be used if adequate information is unavailable

- there is a limited number of standard fixings that cater for the construction tolerances actually encountered on site

- inadequate technical information with regard to installation and performance of fixings.

Design issues

- Failure to involve specialist suppliers in the design, resulting in a cladding fixing system that is difficult to build or has inappropriate tolerances (early discussion with specialist suppliers is essential)

- inadequate information about the physical and chemical environment leading to unsuitable material selection and future corrosion problems

- components and fixings detailed by inexperienced designers, resulting in manufacturing and installation problems, eg thickness of sheeting rails chosen that are adequate to carry loads but not to resist pull-out of fixings

- changes to specification resulting in use of fixings that fail to meet performance requirements

- inadequate drawings and specification, leading to incorrect order for components and fixings and incorrect installation

- lack of installation technical information shown on the details of components and fixings, provided for the fixer/installer, eg for post-drilled anchors, appropriate drill diameter and hole depth, packing shim sizes and maximum thickness, bolt-tightening torque, position of cramps, ties, angles etc

- inadequate setting out of information on drawings, leading to incorrect location of components and fixings

- changes in the construction programme or non-availability of the cladding elements at the required time, which alter the erection sequence. These changes may require the components and fixings or sequence of assembly to be reassessed

- excessive variety in the size and type of components and fixings, leading to the components and fixings being used in the wrong location.

Installation issues

- Failure to install the specified fixings in the correct locations or omission of some fixings to speed up the programme

- failure to instruct the installers/fixers correctly

- allowing the erection sequence to be altered without consideration of the possible consequences

- incorrect hole size formed or wrong anchors installed

- failure to use a torque spanner to tighten all anchors

- cutting or drilling holes and mortices in the cladding or structure of the wrong size and wrong location

- anchors loose due to:
    - incorrect installation torque applied
    - incorrectly mixed or cured resin
    - inadequate hole cleaning
    - inappropriate fixings installed into as-built structure
    - inadequate spacing and edge distances leading to the cracking of the base material

- grout-in anchors wedged into installation holes with, for example, a pebble and no grout inserted

- plated mild steel, shot-fired pins or galvanised wood screws used in place of specified stainless-steel fixings

- excessive number of packing shims used or mild steel shims mixed with stainless steel

- to save costs, plastic horseshoe shims used in applications where the designer has specified metal shims

- compression and expansion joints filled with hard material that should have been removed, commonly plastic, wood and mild steel, stopping any movement or causing local splitting of the cladding

- ad hoc or site-amended fixings used to overcome site problems and fixings adapted on site to deal with unexpected changes in the structure

- cast-in-channels, with the polystyrene insert removed or damaged before concreting, filled with grout making them unusable or requiring laborious effort to remove the grout

- incorrect washer sizes allowing metal sheeting to "pull-over" under wind loading

- incorrect washer sealant breaks down after prolonged exposure to the ultra-violet rays from the sun leading to leaks in profiled metal sheeting

- over-tightening of fixings in sheet metal leading to thread-stripping and over-compression of washer seals, allowing ingress of water.

5.2 CORROSION

Corrosion is an unwanted, destructive chemical or electrochemical reaction between a metal and its environment. Once initiated, the corrosion process continues if driven by suitable conditions. A fixing can thus be gradually weakened to a point where it can no longer withstand the loads imposed on it and failure occurs.

Corrosion can occur under a variety of conditions and can take several forms. Contact with potentially corrosive media can be classified under four broad headings:

- using electrochemically dissimilar metals in contact with each other

- chemicals used on site during construction, of which a common example is the acid solutions used as mortar cleaners

- the environment experienced by the fixing system in-service, typically exposure to atmosphere and frequently to water, in the form of condensation or rainwater runoff

- contact with chemicals used during building cleaning and maintenance.

It is important to recognise two general classes of corrosion attack: general and localised corrosion.

General corrosion

General corrosion, as the term implies, involves the near-uniform loss of section with time. It is found most commonly on unprotected steelwork and is usually signalled by the extensive formation of corrosion product, spalling of concrete cover over a rusting, buried member, or rust staining of nearby masonry.

Although it is possible to increase the initial section of a member to make allowance for corrosion losses with time, it is unlikely that this practice would be adopted for building fixings. Unless dealing with a benign environment for which good corrosion rate data are available, such as sound, uncontaminated mortar or concrete, either a corrosion protection coating system or a corrosion resistant material would be selected.

Localised corrosion

This is usually the result of breakdown of small areas of a corrosion protection system, or from galvanic action (see Section 5.2.2). It may result in areas of perforation of a section, particularly in crevices, without significant indication by the formation of corrosion product.

A fixing can be at risk from corrosion due to factors such as: the internal and external environment, design details, material selection, material incompatibilities and the installation method.

This section describes current guidance, the forms of corrosion commonly identified in fixings and provides a basic knowledge and understanding of different corrosion mechanisms. In addition, general guidance on corrosion control of specific fixings materials under specific conditions is also provided.

5.2.1   Current guidance

Guidance is available to cladding fixing designers and specifiers from a variety of documents. They are produced by cladding system manufacturers, trade associations, material suppliers and independent bodies. Some of the major sources of information on corrosion that should be consulted are described below.

- BRE Information Papers IP12/90 and 13/90: *Corrosion of steel wall ties*
  Specific advice on the corrosion of wall ties.

- BSI: BS5427: Part 1: 1996: *Code of practice for the use of profiled sheet for roof and wall cladding on buildings*
  Advises on the compatibility of materials.

- BS EN ISO 3506-1:1998: *Mechanical properties of corrosion-resistant stainless steel fasteners*
  Advises on classes of corrosion-resistant fasteners.

- BSI: BS7371: *Coatings on metal fasteners*
  Covers the performance of coatings on metal fasteners and accessories.

- BSI: PD 6484: *Commentary on corrosion at bimetallic contacts and its alleviation*
  Guidance on how to avoid bimetallic corrosion.

- The National Federation of Roofing Contractors: *Profiled sheet metal roofing and cladding, a guide to good practice*
  Guidance specifically aimed at sheet metal fixings.

- The Steel Construction Institute: *Architects guide to stainless steel*
  Provides basic information about potential stainless-steel corrosion.

- The Steel Construction Institute: *Curtain wall connections to steel frames*
  Advises on materials to separate dissimilar metals.

- The Steel Construction Institute: *Design of stainless steel fixings and ancillary components*
  Concise advice on durability and corrosion.

5.2.2   Different corrosion mechanisms

This section considers the major causes of corrosion that might affect cladding fixings. Corrosion is an extremely complex subject and it is neither possible nor relevant to cover all the factors in detail in this document. The aim of this section is to outline the basic problems that can occur in the corrosion of fixings and give guidance on how to avoid or mitigate these problems. It may be prudent to seek further advice from a corrosion expert.

Atmospheric corrosion

Atmospheric corrosion is caused by intermittent wetting and drying of exposed surfaces as a result of precipitation and condensation, often in the presence of pollutants in the atmosphere. Factors determining the severity of an environment include time of wetness and the presence of aggressive pollutants, principally chlorides in marine locations and sulphur oxides in industrial atmospheres. Airborne particulates generally increase corrosion risks by forming crevicing poultices but may, in certain cases, form an inert, semi-protective layer.

The severity of atmospheric corrosion by location in the UK has been assessed over many years in a test programme based on measuring the attack of zinc coupons. This information is available in, for example, the *Steelwork protection guide* of the UK Galvanisers' Association, and indicates the broad areas of higher corrosion risk.

It may be necessary to assess microclimates caused by various conditions, such as proximity to salt water, chemicals and industrial plants and the nature of prevailing winds. The extent to which the fixing components are protected from direct contact with the environment is also important. Fully exposed, washed and drained features may pose less risk than partly sheltered features, where washing is less effective and dirt and poultices can build up.

Although not strictly a factor of the atmospheric environment, consideration may also need to be given to the leaching of compounds from structural materials, or the drain-off of corrosion products from other features into fixings locations. A cause of rust staining on exposed stainless steel members can be corrosion product drain-off, or surface deposition of iron-containing dusts.

Galvanic corrosion

Galvanic corrosion can occur when electrochemically dissimilar metals are in contact. It can be avoided by recognising where there may be a risk, and taking precautions in the design and installation of fixings.

When two different metals are in electrical contact with each other in an environment containing water or another electrolyte, they form what is termed a "galvanic couple". One of the metals will corrode more than the other and this is governed by the relative position of the two metals in the galvanic series, as shown in Table 5.1. Corrosion of the least noble metal is increased and the corrosion of the more noble is decreased. The extent of corrosion depends, among other things, on the time of wetness, conductivity of the water, temperature, (presence of dissolved salts) and the relative surface areas of the two metals exposed. If the more noble metal has a larger surface area, more corrosion of the less noble metal must be expected.

Table 5.1 *Galvanic series for fresh water*

Anodic, least noble
Magnesium
Zinc
Aluminium
Carbon steel and cast iron
Copper alloys
Stainless steels[*]
Graphite
Cathodic, most noble

[*] In the passive state, protected by the oxide film. Stainless steels are more active if the oxide film is removed by localised corrosive attack.

Table 5.1 shows the relative behaviour of different materials in fresh water (slight differences in ranking may be found in other media). The vertical separation shows the electrical driving force for reaction. There would be a relatively small tendency for copper to corrode preferentially when coupled to stainless steel. However, there is a greater driving force for dissolving magnesium or zinc when coupled to steel. (This provides the basis of the protection of galvanised steels by the "sacrificial" zinc layer.) These relationships hold under normal conditions, but the position of stainless steels is changed if there should be localised corrosion creating an "active" metal surface. A more detailed description of interactions is given in Table 5.2.

An example of galvanic corrosion risk is the use of a carbon steel or galvanised steel fastener in a stainless-steel flange or bracket. Here, the ratio of areas of the reactive material (the fastener) to the noble metal (the bracket) is small. This concentrates the attack on the fastener. Conversely, wastage of a carbon-steel plate or bracket located by a stainless-steel fastener would be dispersed over a wider area, making the effects less significant.

Methods of avoiding galvanic corrosion, in order of priority, are:

- materials and design choice: avoid coupling metals at the extremes in Table 5.2. Where possible, design to ensure that the more noble area is small in comparison with the less noble area and that the less noble area has adequate inherent corrosion performance

- insulate the joint electrically, using isolating washers or sleeves. Take care that plastic washers do not exaggerate toe deflection or allow torque relaxation. **Sleeves should be avoided as far as possible, as they prevent bolt bearing**

- coat the joint region to prevent ingress of water. **Ensure adequate coverage onto the noble material, as well as on the less noble material.** If this is difficult, coat only the more noble metal. If only the less noble material is protected, the proximity of the bare, noble material will cause attack at any coating defects to be severe.

Galvanic behaviour can be used to provide protection against corrosion. Deliberate coupling of a protective "sacrificial anode" material, at the correct potential separation in Table 5.1, will result in preferential corrosion of the anode and protection of the more noble material. For example, a carbon-steel component could be protected by a zinc or magnesium anode. However, this approach is of limited value for fixing systems as the anode material must be replaced at a frequency depending upon the corrosion conditions. Further guidance on this subject can be found in BS PD 6484.

Crevice corrosion

Crevice corrosion is a considerable problem for fixings. This is a localised type of attack, which occurs in very narrow openings or crevices between metal to metal or non-metal to metal components. Alloys with good resistance to atmospheric corrosion may be prone to crevice corrosion.

A true corrosion crevice is very small, in a range of 0.025–0.1 mm wide. The method by which corrosion takes place is related to these small dimensions, which allow water to enter, but restrict oxygen diffusion.

Crevices fall into two categories: man-made and naturally occurring. Some man-made crevices, which may result during fabrication and assembly, can be avoided by careful design. Examples are screw threads, rivets, lap joints, non-radiused corners, notches and surface cracks. However, some of them may serve a particular design purpose and therefore can be unavoidable. Naturally occurring crevices are often formed by debris such as sand falling onto fixings and lying on the surface of the metal for long periods.

Figure 5.1 shows details that assist in the formation of crevice corrosion, and should be avoided.

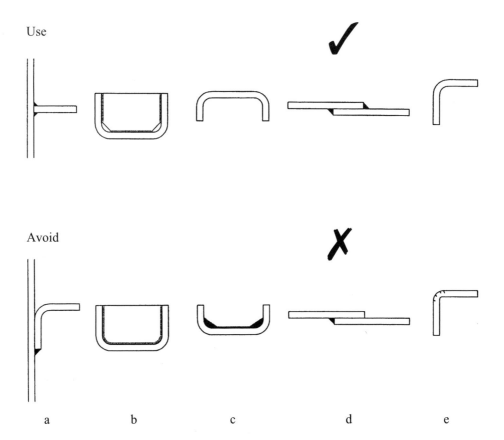

Avoidance of crevices:

a   avoid traps for dirt and water
b   allow drainage paths in channels with stiffeners
c   use channels inverted if possible
d   ensure that lapped joints are sealed to avoid crevices
e   avoid non-radiused corners

Figure 5.1   *Corrosion risk – detail design principles*

Pitting corrosion

Pitting corrosion is an extremely localised corrosive attack that produces relatively small holes and can lead to the perforation of a metallic section. Small holes are serious in water pipes and liquid containers, but can be of less significance for cladding fixings unless they form a site for other forms of ongoing corrosion. Pits can be widely spaced or close together, creating a rough corrosion surface.

Pitting corrosion can occur in most commonly used metals and alloys as a result of the local breakdown of a surface protective layer, whether this is a natural passive film or applied corrosion protection. Chemical contaminants, such as chlorides or marine locations, can increase the risk of pitting attack. For this reason, hydrochloric acid mortar-cleaning solutions must not be allowed to come into contact with stainless-steel fixings. Pitting can also be initiated on stainless steels as a result of embedded carbon-steel fragments from contact with non stainless steel tools.

Stress corrosion cracking

Stress corrosion cracking (SCC) is a term used to describe crack-induced failures in engineering materials that occur by a combination of a tensile stress and a specific corrosive medium. High humidity and high temperature can also be contributory factors. The stresses causing cracking may not be those arising in-service, but can be residual stresses from cold working or thermal cycles during welding. This type of failure is uncommon in construction applications but is known to occur in certain circumstances, such as aggressive environments.

5.2.3 How to avoid corrosion – by material

This section briefly describes the types of corrosion to which most common fixing materials are susceptible. At the same time, methods to minimise the risk of corrosion are suggested.

Stainless steels

Stainless steels are classified as iron-base alloys containing at least 10.5 per cent chromium (Cr). The surface exposed to the atmosphere develops a chromium-based passive oxide layer. This layer is stable under most atmospheric conditions and has the ability to reform if it is damaged by mechanical contact. Thus, under normal circumstances, stainless steels do not require additional corrosion protection treatments. With increasing Cr content and with added nickel (Ni) and molybdenum (Mo) alloying elements, stainless steels can provide excellent corrosion resistance in a variety of environments. As a result of their excellent corrosion resistance, stainless steels are widely used for cladding fixings.

Although atmospheric corrosion resistance of almost all grades of stainless steel is normally high in most environments, they are susceptible to several forms of localised corrosion, such as pitting corrosion, crevice corrosion and, more rarely, stress corrosion cracking (SCC). The corrosion attack can be avoided or minimised by appropriate design and material (grades) selection for specific conditions. Specialist advice should be sought when stainless-steel fixings are used in aggressive environments. Crevices should be avoided and, where this is not possible, they should be appropriately sealed. Free wetting and draining of stainless steel surfaces is desirable to prevent the build up of deposits. Stagnant water regions and dirt traps can promote crevice corrosion and pitting. Higher Cr, and especially higher Mo, grades are more resistant to crevice attack, especially in high temperature areas.

Where the design or environment makes pitting corrosion more likely, specifying more highly alloyed grades may be prudent. For example, the 1.4436 steel has a higher molybdenum content and hence a greater resistance to pitting and crevice corrosion than the related 1.4401 grade.

Austenitic stainless steels realise their full corrosion resistance in the annealed condition with a good standard of surface finish. Performance in aggressive environments may be impaired by heavy cold working, or by the formation of rough, micro-creviced surfaces.

All grades of stainless steels exhibit significantly higher resistance to pitting corrosion than carbon steels in chloride contaminated concrete.

Carbon steels

Carbon-steel fixings can be prone to many forms of corrosion, depending on their design and the environment to which they are exposed. Atmospheric and localised (crevice and pitting) corrosion attacks are the most common. Galvanic corrosion can occur when steel is coupled with other metals or alloys. Despite this, carbon-steel fixings are still suitable in controlled environments.

For fixings and fixing components, the most common form of protection from corrosion is achieved by the use of coatings. For sheet metal, self-tapping fixings can be protected with epoxy or polymer coatings, which need to be able to withstand the abrasive action as the fixing forms a thread in a steel substrate. Metallic coatings are mostly applied either by **hot dipping** into a molten bath of metal or by **electroplating** in an aqueous electrolyte.

Zinc coatings (of which hot-dipped galvanising is one example) protect steel from corrosion by two methods: firstly by forming a barrier between the steel and the corrosive environment; secondly, and more importantly, by galvanically protecting the steel by preferentially corroding. The service life of the zinc coating is generally in direct proportion to the thickness of the coating applied. The coating is comparatively soft and can be damaged, for example, when tightening bolts. Allowances should be made for retouching the fixings with zinc paint.

Galvanised fixings should not be placed in contact with copper or brass materials in a moist environment, as this coupling would result in rapid bimetallic corrosion of zinc (see Section 5.2.2). Where these two materials have to be used together, they should be electrically insulated. With aluminium or stainless steel, the performance of zinc is good if the environment is dry. In humid conditions electrical insulation may be required. This can be achieved by separating the metals with gaskets, bushes and coatings of PTFE, neoprene or nylon. In dry conditions, paint is often adequate.

Aluminium hot-dip coatings (aluminising) also provide carbon-steels with resistance to corrosion. Aluminium coatings protect steel from corrosion by forming a very resistant barrier between the corrosive atmosphere and the steel. The aluminium oxide that forms on the aluminium surface is highly resistant to a wide range of environments. In many environments, aluminium protects steels galvanically in a similar way to zinc.

Aluminium and aluminium alloys

Aluminium owes its excellent corrosion resistance to a passive oxide film barrier on its surface. The oxide film, if damaged, reforms immediately in most environments. Under conditions where the oxide film cannot reform, corrosion is rapid.

The atmospheric corrosion resistance of most aluminium alloys is excellent as they do not require shelter, protective coatings or maintenance. Corrosion of most alloys by atmospheric attack is restricted to mild surface roughening by shallow pitting. In most atmospheric conditions, the corrosion rate decreases with time to a relatively low, steady state rate. This deceleration of corrosion occurs regardless of alloy composition and type of environment.

Mild surface attack can occur on aluminium that is in contact with alkaline building materials, such as concrete, plaster, mortar and cements. The attack involves the breakdown of the natural oxide films and some of the metal itself. Where aluminium is embedded in concrete, it should be pre-coated with bituminous paint or hot bitumen. Further useful information can be obtained from the Council of Aluminium in Building (see Sources of information).

Some insulation materials, such as polyurethane and glass fibre, may contain corrosive agents that could be extracted under moist conditions and damage the aluminium. Insulating materials should be tested under moist and saline conditions and a sealant, such as bitumen, applied as necessary.

Aluminium is lower in the galvanic series than the other metals in this section. It needs to be separated from these metals to prevent bimetallic corrosion.

Copper and copper alloys

Although copper and copper alloys are susceptible to several forms of corrosion, they exhibit excellent corrosion resistance in many environments. They can resist both atmospheric and localised corrosion, but galvanic corrosion is possible and copper-based metals should not be allowed to contact other common structural metals, such as steel and aluminium.

Applying metallic or organic coatings can increase the corrosion resistance of copper-based metals. Examples of these are coatings of tin and lead, which are applied by hot-dipping and electroplating.

For restraint and load-bearing fixings, copper is typically alloyed to form higher-strength phosphor bronze, aluminium bronze and silicon aluminium bronze materials. Fixings produced from copper alone are not suitable for carrying permanent loads.

Table 5.2 *Guide to corrosion as a result of bimetallic couples (based on the tables given in BSI PD 6484)*

Metal under consideration	Metal in contact with metal under consideration									
	Aluminium	Aluminium bronze	Cast iron	Copper	Phosphor bronze	Lead	Stainless steel (austenitic)	Stainless steel (martensitic)	Steel	Zinc
Aluminium		1	0	1	1	0	0	0	1	0
		3	1	3	3	0	1	1	1	0
		3	2	3	3	3	2	2	3	0
Aluminium bronze	0	–	0	0	0	0	0	0	0	0
	0	–	0	0	0	0	0	0	0	0
	0	–	0	0	0	0	0	0	0	0
Cast iron	0	1	–	1	1	0	1	1	0	0
	0	1	–	2	2	1	2	2	0	0
	0	1	–	2	2	1	2	2	0	0
Copper	0	0	0	–	0	0	0	0	0	0
	0	0	0	–	0	0	0	0	0	0
	0	0	0	–	0	0	0	0	0	0
Phosphor bronze	0	0	0	0	–	0	0	0	0	0
	0	0	0	0	–	0	0	0	0	0
	0	0	0	0	–	0	0	0	0	0
Lead	0	0	0	0	0	–	0	0	0	0
	0	0	0	0	0	–	0	0	0	0
	0	1	0	1	1	–	1	1	0	0
Stainless steel (austenitic)	0	0	0	0	0	0	–	0	0	0
	0	1	1	1	0	1	–	0	0	0
	0	1	–	2	0	1	–	1	1	0
Stainless steel (martensitic)	0	0	0	–	0	0	0	–	0	0
	0	1	0	1	0	0	1	–	1	0
	0	1	0	1	0	0	1	–	1	0
Steel	0	3	1	2	2	1	1	1		0
	0	3	1	2	2	1	–	1		0
	0	3	2	3	3	1	3	3		0
Zinc	0	1	1	1	1	0	1	1	1	–
	1	1	1	2	1	1	1	1	1	–
	1	2	2	2	2	1	1	1	2	–

Key
The degree of corrosion will vary with the type of atmospheric exposure so there are three readings for each fixing metal:

Rural
Industrial/urban
Marine

0   Metal will suffer either no additional corrosion or only slight additional corrosion, usually tolerable in service
1   Metal will suffer slight or moderate corrosion which may be tolerable in some circumstances
2   Metal will suffer fairly severe corrosion and protective measures will usually be necessary
3   Metal may suffer severe additional corrosion and the contact should be avoided
–   No evidence available, no guidance can be given.

NB These are the definitions given in PS 6484: 1979, *Commentary on corrosion at bimetallic contacts and its alleviation.*
When using the table, both metals should be considered.

Example
For a steel fixing into copper, the table above shows for steel: 2   for copper: 0
                                                                  2   0
                                                                  3   0

In a **rural** environment the fixing may suffer fairly severe corrosion and protective measures will usually be necessary.
In an **industrial/urban** environment the fixing may suffer fairly severe corrosion and protective measures will usually be necessary.
In a **marine** environment the fixing may suffer severe additional corrosion and the contact should be avoided.
The copper will not suffer significant corrosion.

6 Good practice guidance

6.1 DESIGN PARAMETERS

The correct design of fixings between cladding panels and the main structure is a critical factor in the successful performance of the building. It has to enable efficient and rapid construction as well as providing sound, durable structural and physical properties. It is therefore important that fixings are considered at an early stage of the design.

The information required to design the fixings will be jointly agreed by the architect, structural engineer and cladding designer, with some input from the material and trade contractors. The three main parties must clearly define the person with overall responsibility for the design and specification of fixings.

The design of the cladding must be co-ordinated with the design of the main structure to ensure that loads are not unintentionally transferred to the cladding. In precast concrete panel and panelised curtain wall systems it is possible that some of the lateral restraint forces from the main structure may be transferred to the cladding. If the panels are not designed to cater for these forces, the design of fixings must ensure that any transfer of forces is avoided.

The Construction (Design and Management) Regulations 1994 require construction designers to have regard for the health and safety of any person carrying out construction or cleaning work in or on the structure, or any other person who may be affected by this work. The Regulations define the terms "designer" and "construction" to have much wider meanings than those in common usage. As well as architects and engineers, "designer" includes surveyors, clients (where they specify particular requirements), project managers, specialist suppliers and contractors, and temporary works designers. "Construction work" includes maintenance, repair, demolition and dismantling. The duties on designers apply to all construction work, regardless of size or duration, even when other parts of the Regulations do not (see CIRIA Report 166 *CDM Regulations – work sector guidance for designers*).

Aspects of cladding, published by the Institution of Structural Engineers, gives very good advice on cladding design in general, which can be related to the design of fixings and secondary support components.

The logical sequence for the design is:

- agree and obtain the information that is required to design the cladding fixing system
- design the most suitable fixing arrangement that best meets the performance specification
- select and specify a suitable fixing.

6.1.1 Information required

In order to design the fixings between a cladding system and the supporting structure, the following information will be required:

Site location

This includes information on geographical location, proximity of adjacent buildings, vicinity of the sea, and the type and use of building. The area surrounding a building can have a significant effect on the wind loading (see BS 6399: Part 2). Examples of this are buildings that are located at the tops of embankments, or the presence of narrow gaps between neighbouring buildings, which lead to higher wind speeds. Clearly the height and shape of the building itself will also have an effect on the wind loading applied to the cladding, which can result in high, localised forces on the cladding. The fixings must meet the maximum requirements.

Life expectancy

This needs to be specified by the client in relation to the building's use and location. The life expectancy of the fixing cannot be considered independently; it needs to be carried out in conjunction with the rest of the building, ie primary structure, cladding type etc. Manufacturers should be asked to provide details of average life expectancy for different fixings. BS 7543 *Durability of buildings and building elements, products and components* gives guidance on the durability required and the predicted service life and design life of buildings and their components and/or parts. It is applicable to new buildings rather than applications and repair. Tables 1 and 2 from the Standard define different life categories for buildings and components respectively.

Structure and cladding type

Full knowledge of the type of structure is required in order to design suitable fixings, eg steel frame, concrete frame, precast concrete frame, composite concrete/metal decking, *in situ* concrete slab/edge beams, precast concrete planks with *in situ* topping, timber frame, masonry etc. Positions of movement joints will also influence the fixing positions and details.

The materials of the cladding and structure that have to be penetrated, or have to be in contact with each other, must be known so that suitable fixings and separators may be selected to avoid problems of bimetallic corrosion.

Construction tolerances

This is a critical feature of the buildability aspect and, if handled incorrectly, can have considerable consequences and significant cost implications. When establishing tolerances, it is important to ensure that they are achievable by all those involved in the construction process. If British Standard structural tolerances are considered unacceptable, the architect, structural engineer, main contractor, structural frame contractor and cladding contractor should jointly agree the alternative. Advice should be taken from BS 5606 *Code of practice for accuracy in building* and CIRIA Technical Note 113, *A suggested design procedure for accuracy in buildings*.

The DETR has recently addressed the issue of inadequate management of tolerances, which frequently occurs in practice. They and the construction industry have researched methods to promote better management of the tolerances required at the building/ cladding interface and the results are due to be published in 2000. Good guidance is also provided in the Steel Construction Institute publication *Curtain wall connections to steel frames*, which addresses the subject of interfaces.

Structural load capacity

The fixings must be designed to withstand the worst load scenarios. The following types of load must be considered: dead loads, wind loads, impact loads, temporary loads during construction and loading caused by vibration etc. If the client requests it, the structural engineer might also consider bomb blast loads. Thorough guidance on this subject is given in the Institution of Structural Engineers' *Aspects of cladding*, referred to in Section 4.

Environmental conditions

The environment is considered so that any unusual conditions that could promote corrosion may be identified, such as the type and internal use of the building, temperature, humidity, aggressive environmental aspects from industrial processes etc. The location of the fixings in relation to vapour barriers and insulation layers also needs to be considered, to try to avoid condensation. Advice on the relevance of known pollutants should be sought from a corrosion expert.

Maintenance

Internal access is disruptive so the design should aim to make the fixings maintenance-free. It should, however, be possible to carry out visual inspections of the fixings as part of the maintenance programme. This might require demountable inner wall linings, for example, or methods to view the fixings by use of fibre-optic probes.

Access method

The designer needs to understand the proposed access method for installing and maintaining the cladding and the fixings. This might be from an external scaffold or from hoist access platforms, or a moveable plant such as cherry-pickers or scissor lifts. Some cladding is installed from the inside of the building only, without the use of external access systems.

6.1.2 Design

When all of the information detailed above has been obtained, the fixings can be designed. This section details the design considerations that have to be addressed.

The fixings should always be considered in the early concept design stage and ideally the fixing manufacturer and/or cladding subcontractor and fixing consultant should be involved at this stage.

In Section 2, the difference between primary and secondary fixings was defined. Reference should be made to Figure 2.2, which shows a generic section of the different components involved in a cladding fixing assembly.

Dead and live loads

All the possible critical loads acting on the structure and the cladding need to be considered and the fixing specified for the combined worst case. This should include the loads considered in Section 6.1.1 and the additional loads resulting from movements of the structure. The effect of shrinkage and creep must also be considered. Shrinkage will diminish with time and its effect on the cladding fixings will depend on the time between the structure being erected and the cladding being fixed.

Movements

Before designing fixing connections, it is important to know the anticipated relative movements between the cladding and structure. These will occur due to:

- thermal effects (excluding fire) – the differential expansion of the cladding and the shielded structure
- structural settlement – settlement of foundations causing distortion of the structure
- natural shrinkage or expansion – shrinkage of a drying concrete structure and expansion or shrinkage of cladding materials like bricks
- creep – the long-term effect of gravity on concrete structures
- normal building dynamics, such as sway resulting from wind loading
- imposed loads on the floors/beams leading to differential movement of the top and bottom restraints of a cladding panel.

The fixings have to be able to accommodate these movements. Particular attention should be paid to the movement joints that are an integral part of the structure.

The facing materials will tend to have more joints than the main building structure. The design must ensure that the joints in the cladding coincide with the joints in the building structure.

Compatibility with other building components

The cladding cannot be considered in isolation from the other building components, such as the cavity drainage trays, window fixings, raised floor pedestals and under-floor services. The fixing designer will need to co-ordinate with other designers, and the build-up of tolerance allowances of the components should be considered.

Fire resistance

The fixings must be able to withstand a fire duration that is agreed in advance with the statutory authorities and the additional loads on the fixings during fire conditions will need to be considered. These will result from differential expansion of materials etc.

For any application requiring a fire rating of any significance, eg above half an hour, special measures must be taken. There are a variety of approaches, all of which are detailed in *Fixings and fire*, published by the Construction Fixings Association.

Briefly, the measures are as follows:

- the application of additional fire protection must protect the base material over the whole zone of influence of the fixing, ie typically over a radius of twice the embedment depth, rather than a radius equivalent to the thickness of the protection layer

- fixings can be specified based on manufacturer's test data, with loads certified for specific durations of exposure. Several manufacturers have had a wide variety of fixings tested to ISO/DIN fire curves, resulting in certified loads for exposures of 30–120 minutes. Some anchors may be specified for 30 minutes without reduction from normal recommended loads. Loads for 120 minutes are usually reduced significantly

- stainless-steel anchors generally offer better fire resistance than carbon-steel anchors. As fire resistance is often determined by failure of the bolt head or nut at the surface, resin-bonded injection anchors offer very similar resistance to all-steel anchors. The resistance of resin anchors may be increased to match that of the nut at the surface by increasing embedment depth.

Corrosion resistance

The subject of corrosion resistance was explained in Section 5.2, where guidance was provided on potential problems and how to avoid them. The basic considerations are always the prevention of contact with water deposits, pollutants, leachates from building materials and contact between dissimilar metals. It may be prudent to seek expert advice.

Buildability

At all times during the design, the designer should consider the method of installing the fixings and cladding. This should be during first installation, maintenance and possible replacement within the service life of the building. Feedback on the success of previous designs should always be sought and incorporated in the development of improved solutions. Safe access for all work is required and must be considered as part of the design.

Figure 6.1 shows an example of when this was not achieved: the design did not permit the use of a top mechanical fixing and resin was used instead to fix the stone panel to the bracket.

Figure 6.1   *An example of poor design co-ordination and poor supervision*

Similarly, Figure 6.2 is an example of poor design and workmanship in stone cladding. Insufficient edge distance for a mechanical fixing resulted in spalling of the edge and unsafe connection.

Figure 6.2   *An example of poor design and workmanship in stone cladding*

Simple issues, such as reducing the numbers and varieties of fixings, can have significant advantages on site by minimising loss and the possibility of using the wrong fixing.

6.1.3   Selection and specification

Following completion of the design, suitable fixings are selected and specified. These are based on manufacturers' published data sheets, which define the properties and performance of fixings. There are many factors which need to be taken into account when specifying anchors of any type, cast-in or post-installed:

- the magnitude of applied load in relation to recommended or approved load
- the direction of applied load, tension, shear or bending (taking account of packing or shims)
- the condition of base material, eg if concrete is it cracked or non-cracked
- the strength of base material
- the structural thickness of base material
- edge and spacing criteria
- anchor positioning with respect to reinforcement
- the fixture thickness (taking account of packing)
- corrosion conditions (see Section 5.2).

The Construction Fixings Association's publication, *Anchor selection*, details many of these points.

Selection should always be carried out using the manufacturer's published data. Such data should detail all the above parameters and be authenticated by an approval certificate or test certificates from independent, accredited test laboratories. If in any doubt about any aspect of selection, the manufacturer should be involved and asked to recommend the appropriate fixing.

Anchors issued with a European Technical Approval in accordance with ETAG 001 *Guideline for European Technical Approvals of metal anchors for use in concrete* or a similar recognised national approval such as an Agrément certificate will, if specified and installed in accordance with the qualifications of the approval document, satisfy the requirements of Subsection A1, *Loading*, in Building Regulations (1991) Approved Document A *Structures*.

Changes in specification of proprietary anchors should only be made if all the original design parameters are satisfied by the proposed alternative.

When selecting fixings for a particular project, the risk of errors is reduced if the same manufacturer supplies all fixing components. The number of different fixings used on any project should be minimised. The specification should comprise material details and component dimensions, and detailed drawings clearly demonstrating the fixing method should be available on site.

The specification and drawings must be comprehensive and should include:

- the constituent material of all parts
- the dimensions of all parts
- tests required in advance of the fixings use.

Drawings should be to the standard illustrated in Section 3 and include:

- manufacturer's name
- full anchor designation and catalogue number
- hole diameter and depth
- setting tools (setting punch, drill bits etc)
- curing time for bonded injection anchors
- tightening torque.

As stated earlier, it is important that the responsibility for the design and specification of fixings is clearly defined. For example, if secondary fixings are to be designed by the specialist subcontractor (such as the curtain wall contractor or the sheet metal supplier), the specification below could apply.

6.1.4 Typical performance specification

The following is an example of a typical performance specification (reproduced with the permission of Cladtech Associates).

1.0. Anchorage and Fixing Supports:

1.0.1. *All anchorages and supports shall be designed, fabricated and installed for full compliance with all the performance criteria herein specified, including the accommodation of thermal, wind pressure and all other building dynamics, without hazard to any curtain walling components or assemblies, glass and glazing and related sealant applications.*

1.0.2. *The Sub-Contractor shall design the anchorage and fixing supports as specified above and in full conformance with the performance and site requirements.*

1.0.3. *The curtain walling shall be fixed at points designated on the Sub-Contractor's drawings and approved by the Architect and Structural Engineer.*

1.0.4.   The curtain wall components shall be fixed to the structure using bracket components of alloyed steel, aluminium alloy or rolled steel sections as agreed with the Building Inspector. They must comply with all statutory requirements both as to strength and type and shall be designed to carry all dead, live and wind loadings.

Alloyed steel shall be austenitic stainless steel type to BS EN 10088 Parts 1, 2 & 3.

Extruded aluminium sections and aluminium rolled plate materials used for bracket construction shall be from structural quality aluminium as defined in BS 8118 1991. All hole sizes shall make allowance for any sleeving necessary.

All bracket constructions and fixings shall be fully protected to prevent corrosion and any bi-metallic degradation that may occur due to dissimilar metals being in contact generally in accordance with the provisions of BS PD 6484: 1984.

1.0.5.   Any sheet steel, cleats, angles, etc. used in the fixing assemblies shall comply with BS 7668: 1994 and rolled sections shall be used wherever practicable or appropriate.

Any rolled steel or sheet steel used for brackets, cleats, angles, etc. in the fixing assemblies are to be fully protected against corrosion by hot dip galvanising in accordance with BS 729: 1971 and BS 5493: 1977 or by shot blasting and Zinc spraying. "On site" rust proofing shall not be allowed.

1.0.6.   Bolts, screws and nuts, used for the curtain wall assemblies and for fixings to the structure, shall be of adequate strength for their design purpose and shall be austenitic stainless steel, to BS 6105 with strength classification/ minimum strength.

They shall be used in accordance with the manufacturer's recommendations and bolts' and fixings' failure loads will have been substantiated by previous tests.

Random tests may be required to be carried out on site on up to 10% of the fixing bolts to the structure, to prove that the fixing bolts are performing to the specified standards. These tests will be proof load tests and not ultimate tests to failure.

Full consideration shall be given to the effects of 'torque relaxation' following initial tightening. If necessary the bolts shall be re-tightened in order to restore the torque levels to within bolt manufacturer's published limits.

It will be the Sub-Contractor's responsibility to execute such tests to the satisfaction of the Architect and Structural Engineer.

1.0.7.   The Sub-Contractor shall be responsible for supplying and fixing all necessary anchors and supports for the complete installation. The Sub-Contractor is to allow for all necessary drilling to the structure and for the supply and fixing of stainless steel bolts and attachments.

1.0.8.   Details depicting the design, materials, location and installation procedures of all anchorage and fixing supports shall be fully documented on the working drawings.

1.0.9.   If any fixing bracket assemblies occur within a "wetted" zone, these are to be constructed from either austenitic stainless steel, to BS EN 10088 or structural quality aluminium alloy to BS 8118 1991. A wetted zone is a zone located to the outside of the designed wet plane of the glazing system.

1.0.10. Loads shall not be carried on slots that run in the direction of the load unless provision for restoring positive fixity is incorporated.

1.0.11. Where specified due to special requirements, all bolts shall be equipped with locking nuts.

1.0.12. Anchorages and support fixing assemblies shall be shown and described and scheduled on the shop drawings. The description shall include all movements and tolerances of related building, curtain wall and associated works components.

1.0.13. Site installation and inspection personnel shall be provided with a schedule of assembly and erection tolerances, thermal and all other loading tolerances herein specified.

Due allowance for the cumulative effect of all tolerances (fabrication, assembly, thermal, building and erection) shall be made to ensure complete conformity with design requirements.

1.0.14. 100% visual inspection of all anchorage and support fixing assemblies shall be carried out by the Sub-Contractor and certified records shall be kept by the Sub-Contractor for inspection by the Main Contractor.

1.0.15. Completely concealed fixing methods shall be adopted as a principle throughout the work. If in isolated cases face fixings are unavoidable, particular care shall be taken to locate these in unobtrusive positions, where heads of screws, bolts, etc. shall be countersunk and finished to match the adjoining exposed aluminium surfaces. All such fixings shall be specifically brought to the attention of the Architect for approval before being executed.

1.0.16. A comprehensive checklist shall be provided for the use of the site installation team. The list will uniquely number each bay and clearly identify all critical installation steps. Each step shall require a tick to be inserted against it to signify satisfactory completion of the check or operation prior to commencing the next operation in the sequence. Inspection "Hold" points shall be incorporated. Copies of the checklist shall be countersigned by the resident supervisor and the Main Contractor's representative. Copies of completed lists shall be retained on site.

1.0.17 All marking out, cutting away, drilling, plugging and fixing shall be by the Sub-Contractor.

1.0.18 No drilling or cutting of steel, concrete or timber shall be carried out without the prior approval of the Main Contractor.

The sketches in Section 3 show generic systems and the way in which they are connected to the structure. The available options, and the advantages and disadvantages of each, are detailed in Table 6.1.

Table 6.1 *Key advantages and disadvantages of different types of fixings (continued on following page)*

Fixing type	Key advantages	Key disadvantages
Cast-in channels for *in situ* **or precast concrete structures**	Load can be better distributed by arranging reinforcement around the cast-in channel. Suitable for concrete that may become cracked, ie tension zones. May be loaded as soon as concrete is cured. If the channels are correctly positioned, the fixing operation for brackets is faster than for methods requiring hole drilling. No electric power required when attaching fixtures. May be designed to allow positioning close to edges if the reinforcement is set between cast-in element and the edge (see Section 6.2.1 for clarification).	Additional cost involved in positioning channels before concreting. Reinforcement steel must be designed to allow room for the cast-in element. Channels may be displaced during concrete placement.
Cast-in sockets for *in situ* **or precast concrete structures**	As above. Lower cost.	As above. No adjustment possible for fixing location.
Post-installed expansion anchors for concrete structures	Suitable for lightly reinforced concrete. Some types approved for tension zones, ie cracked concrete. No costs during concreting. May be loaded immediately. May be installed in wet weather conditions. Serviceable at high ambient temperatures. Bolt or complete anchorage may be removable depending on type.	Consideration at design stage or cover meter checks at installation advisable to avoid reinforcement in heavily reinforced structures. High expansion stresses mean restrictions on close edge and spacing dimensions. Performance reduced in weak materials. Functioning may be affected if subjected to impact or vibration loads.
Post-installed undercut anchors for concrete structures	Developed for use in concrete which may become cracked ie tension zones. Suitable for lightly reinforced concrete. Lack of expansion stresses allows closer edge and spacing dimensions. No costs during concreting. May be loaded immediately. May be installed in wet weather conditions. Serviceable in high ambient temperatures. Bolt may be removable depending on type.	Consideration at design stage or cover meter checks at installation advisable to avoid reinforcement in heavily reinforced structures. May incur additional drilling costs depending on type. Additional cost involved in under-cutting process.

Fixing type	Key advantages	Key disadvantages
Post-installed bonded injection anchors for concrete structures	Suitable for lightly reinforced concrete. Lack of expansion stresses allows closer edge and spacing dimensions. Good resistance (of resin bond) to dynamic loads. Some types approved for tension zones, ie cracked concrete. Bolt removable, if used with an internally threaded socket. Offers good corrosion resistance. May be used in weak and voided materials, including masonry. No costs during concreting.	Consideration at design stage or cover meter checks at installation advisable to avoid reinforcement in heavily reinforced structures. May not be loaded immediately. Adherence to manufacturer's instructions important for full performance. Reduced performance at elevated temperatures. Some resin types sensitive to wet holes. Limits on installation temperatures. Diamond drilled holes may require roughening operation depending on resin type.
Post-installed bonded injection anchors for blockwork	Special accessories for bonded injection systems allow fixing into hollow and perforated materials. Most appropriate for fixings into blockwork.	Care needed at installation stage to avoid breaking bond by over-tightening.
Post-installed screws with special plastic wall plugs for blockwork	Low cost and simple to install.	Performance is generally low in aerated blocks. Care needed drilling aerated blocks. Not all types suitable for hollow or cellular blocks.
Self-drilling self-tapping fixings for sheet metal	Drilling and taping is carried out in one operation which reduces the total fixing time and also the problems of incorrectly sized holes.	The fixing type and length must be carefully selected as the drilling function must be complete before self-tapping starts.
Thread-forming self-tapping fixings for sheet metal	A larger diameter fastener, with increased resistance to pull out.	Hole must be drilled in advance of fixings. If the pre-drilled hole is undersized, the fixing may not penetrate or the torque required to form the thread may cause overstraining or breakage of the fixing. If the hole is oversized, the fixing will achieve a lower strength.
Stud type lateral restraint fixing	Adjustable after installation to align panels. Can be connected to concrete with cast-in or post-drilled (expanding or bonded) fixings. Can be connected to blockwork using post-drilled fixings.	Lateral restraint only.
Grout-in anchor for lateral restraint and support	Support and lateral restraint of thin stone cladding panels is possible.	Possible error in grout selection and application can lead to a weak fixing.

6.2 INSTALLATION

The questionnaire survey indicated that one of the most common causes of failure results from poor installation and inadequate on-site supervision.

This section provides guidance on how to address this issue by good practice, thus enhancing confidence in the long-term integrity of the cladding fixings.

Only post-installed fixings and cast-in fixings are covered in this section. These types of fixings are installed by general contractors; all other fixings are normally installed by specialist subcontractors. However the principles of this section apply to all fixings, irrespective of who carries out installation.

No statutory requirement exists for any training or certification for those installing fixings, although some fixing manufacturers provide an installation training service for their products. There is a recognised need for independent training, similar to the CWCT certification scheme for curtain walling installers.

6.2.1 Post-installed fixings

Site drilled bolts must be installed in accordance with the manufacturer's instructions, which must be complete and clearly and simply stated within the fixings installation details prepared for each contract. See attached illustrations for further details on installation of bonded and post-installed fixings (Figures 6.3 and 6.4). In addition, for all safety-critical applications, manufacturers must supply a detailed method statement, which should be referred to in the specification and on the drawings. It is important that installers understand the details and have all the necessary components and tools to carry out the work.

A typical installation procedure for post-installed anchors usually consists of the following instructions:

- determine precise location
- drill the hole of the exact diameter to the exact depth
- brush and blow the hole (up to three times; this requirement is more rigorous for bonded than for mechanical anchors)
- insert the fixing in a required manner
- in case of torque-controlled anchors, apply the required torque as given on the drawings by a calibrated torque wrench
- it is beneficial for all bolts to be torqued and for torque values to be listed on installation drawings.

The importance of each of the above steps is further explained in this section.

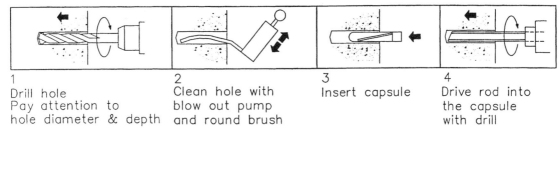

1
Drill hole
Pay attention to
hole diameter & depth

2
Clean hole with
blow out pump
and round brush

3
Insert capsule

4
Drive rod into
the capsule
with drill

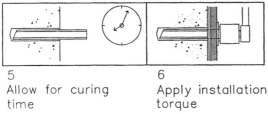

5
Allow for curing
time

6
Apply installation
torque

Figure 6.3   *A good example of installation instructions for bonded anchors*

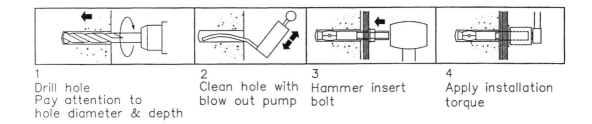

1
Drill hole
Pay attention to
hole diameter & depth

2
Clean hole with
blow out pump

3
Hammer insert
bolt

4
Apply installation
torque

Figure 6.4   *A good example of installation instructions for expansion anchors*

Location

Where post-drilled fixings are used in heavily reinforced concrete, the location of each bolt must be carefully considered at the design stage. However it is good practice to use a cover meter to establish the exact location of the reinforcement as rebar is often out of place. The drawings should provide guidance in the event of the reinforcement being hit: consideration should be given as to whether to cut the rebar or reposition the fixing. Reinforcement should only be cut with the agreement of the structural engineer. If relocation of the fixing is the preferred method, the distance between the aborted hole and the new location should be one of the following:

- the depth of the aborted hole if it is filled with strong non-shrink grout
- twice the depth of the aborted hole if it is not filled
- close to the original hole if the embedment depth of the new hole is increased by the depth of the aborted hole.

Edge distances

It is important that the edge distance requirements, as stated on the drawing, should be achieved. If in reality this cannot be achieved, installation should cease until either a new fixing connection is designed or reduction factor calculations justifying the revised edge distance are produced. In many cases, reduced edge distances may be acceptable, provided that the fixing is still within the reinforcement cage. This should always be checked with the structural engineer. Failure to observe the minimum edge distance requirements or to undertake necessary justification can result in fracturing of the background structure and failure of the fixing component.

The choice of fixing will be influenced by the edge distance requirement. Advantages and disadvantages are shown in Table 6.1. If edge distances are critical, cast-in channel should be considered at the design stage.

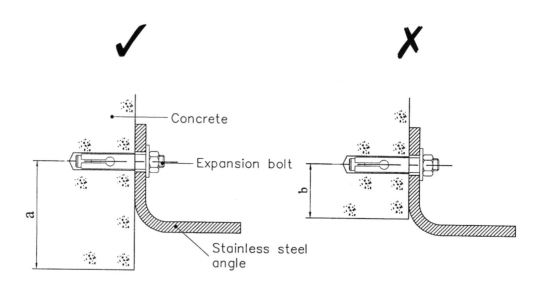

a ≥ minimum edge distance   b < minimum edge distance

Figure 6.5   *Minimum edge distances*

It is important to clarify the difference between characteristic and minimum edge distance. Characteristic edge distance is related to characteristic performance. Minimum edge distance is the minimum at which the anchor can be installed, but at reduced performance. Characteristic edge distance should generally be adhered to. Minimum edge distance and reduced performance should be independently certified.

Drilling

The holes in the structure must be carefully located and drilled to suit the bolt being used. It is important that the hole is drilled to the specified diameter and depth to ensure the correct fit of the bolt. This is equally important for expansion and bonded injection anchors. Worn drill bits should be discarded and replaced with new ones, thus reducing the risk of errors.

Attention must be given to the method of drilling to ensure that the holes are drilled at 90° to the face of the structure.

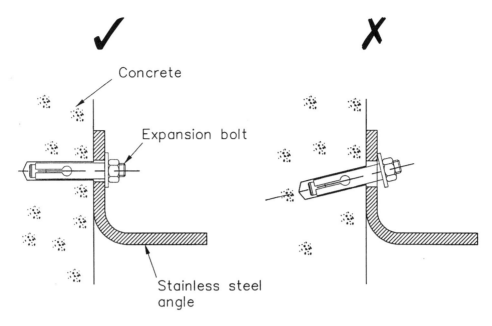

✓ ✗

Concrete

Expansion bolt

Stainless steel
angle

Figure 6.6 *The holes must be drilled at 90° to the face of the structure*

Figure 6.7 *An example of poor workmanship; left-hand side expansion anchor installed at an angle, not 90°*

Hole cleaning

All debris and dust created by the drilling must be removed from the hole. This is generally achieved by brushing and blowing out the hole. Performance of fixings, particularly bonded anchors, may be considerably reduced when installed in a hole that has not been cleaned. Additionally, when bonded systems in solid substrate are used, it is important for some systems that the hole is not damp as this will further reduce the load-bearing capacity of the fixing.

Some bonded injection anchors are available that can be installed in damp holes where excess water has been removed. Due attention should be paid to the increased curing time which will be required. It is particularly important that manufacturer's instructions are followed in these circumstances. In addition, some bonded anchors are approved for installation in damp or even water-filled holes. Again, it is important to follow manufacturer's instructions in these cases. A suitability test in wet holes will be a requirement for the European Technical Approval Guideline (ETAG) Part 5. (This document is described in more detail in Section 6.4).

Tightening

To function properly, torque-controlled expansion anchors and some bonded anchors require tightening. It is absolutely essential that for both restraint and support applications, the correct tightening torque is applied using a calibrated torque spanner. The use of pre-set and calibrated torque spanners with fixed socket heads is essential and, if frequently used, they must be recalibrated at intervals not exceeding three months. When torque spanners for large bolts (say M20 and above) are continuously used, they may require recalibrating more regularly (eg every one or two months). The calibration should be traceable to national standards.

Although it is not essential for proper functioning to torque all bonded injection anchors, they should ideally be set to the manufacturer's recommended torque (manufacturers should provide the installation torque when approached). This is because:

- where the fixture is required to be clamped to the structure, the tightening torque is a means to ensure that the clamping force exceeds the recommended minimum tensile load, ie the fixture will not become loose
- for all fixings the torque is set at a level that will not damage the bolt material. In case of bonded anchors it also protects the bond, which could easily be sheared with a turn or two if the recommended torque is exceeded. This is especially important when bonded anchors are installed in weaker substrates, in which case the torque should be reduced in proportion to the reduction in recommended load. The manufacturer should provide detailed guidance on this.

Under no circumstances should any fixing be over- or under-tightened, as this will adversely affect long-term performance. Over-tightening generates excessive stresses in the bolt material and the base material. In concrete and masonry this may result in local crushing, which has a detrimental effect on the long-term fixings performance. Under-tightening prevents the anchor from setting, thus reducing its ability to develop its full potential. The initial torque will relax with time by up to 50 per cent of its original value and most of the relaxation takes place immediately following tightening of the bolt. However, the experimental work on this subject shows that subsequent retorquing reduces the ultimate relaxation.

If fixings are installed at closer spacings and edge distances than those recommended by the manufacturer, guidance should be sought from the manufacturer on how this affects installation torque.

If the specified tightening torque cannot be achieved, the use of the specified anchor should cease and the cause investigated. The most likely causes are:

- oversized hole caused by the use of a drill bit of the wrong diameter
- undersized hole caused by the use of a worn drill bit, resulting in anchor being hammered into position and the anchor body being damaged, or the specified torque being achieved before the fixing is properly expanded
- hole depth insufficient and bolt projects too far, extra washers used to achieve tightness. Insufficient hole depth can also result in reduced embedment depth and subsequently reduced performance
- inappropriate backing structure for selected fixing; blockwork in lieu of concrete or lightweight concrete used. Bolt does not achieve specified tightening torque due to local crushing of the base material, thus allowing the bolt to slip.

If the bolts have been installed without the use of torque spanners and subsequently over-tightened, they should be removed and replaced.

Packing

One of the frequent examples of bad practice is misuse of packing. Packing involves using thin plates of hard plastic or metal (usually called shims) to locate components to the correct line or level. In this respect, it is important to observe the following rules:

- the thickness and number of shims installed behind any fixing should not exceed the maximum specified by the manufacturer of the fixing used

- the maximum packing thickness will be different for fixings in bending compared to those in tension only

- if the packing thickness exceeds that specified, the bracket should be replaced unless the fixing manufacturer feels able to issue a warranty

- packing should provide full support for any angle or component extending at least to the heel of the angle just below the start of the radius

- packing should not come within 25 mm of the edge of a slab, beam or column, to prevent the risk of spalling.

- plastic or mild steel shims should be used only as specified

- partial packing installed to overcome an out of true structural face should only be used once justified and approved by the responsible engineer.

It is equally important to use adequate washers (particularly over slotted holes). They should be sufficiently thick to transfer the loads adequately and not deform.

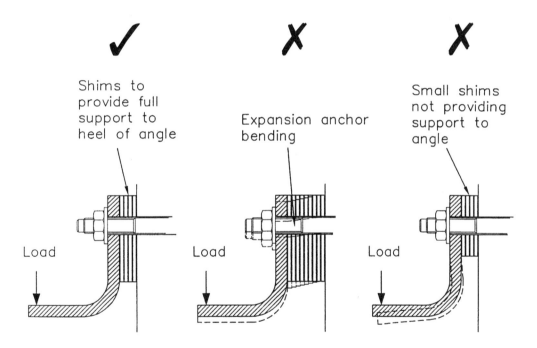

Figure 6.8 *Examples of good and bad packing practice*

6.2.2 Cast-in fixings

Generally, these products are most frequently used in the form of cast-in channels. For successful performance of this type of fixing, it is essential to give careful consideration at the design stage. For example, when used with stone cladding, both the stone joint patterns and the fixing positions should be detailed and agreed before site work begins.

Channels are supplied with bonding lugs. These are normally factory-fitted and are tolerant of rough site handling, but they should not be misused. When the lugs are supplied loose it is important to ensure that they are fitted and bent as required. When lugs are pre-fitted to shape they should not be altered, since this may reduce the pull-out value of the channel.

Cast-in channels should be attached to the inside face of the shutter or suspended to pre-set outriggers. Under no circumstances should they be positioned after concrete is poured.

The fixing to a cast-in channel is completed using a T-head bolt, which should be correctly located in the channel. Most T-bolts have a groove in the stud end so that their orientation can be checked.

With regards to packing, the same rules apply as with the post-drilled fixings, ie it must not exceed the manufacturer's recommended thickness.

Channels formed from thin-gauge material, such as traditional dovetail slots, rely on their shape for bond and are normally used with ties rather than fixing bolts. Care must be taken in handling such products to ensure that there is no damage to their shape, which could affect their performance and the subsequent fit of the ties. When ties are used, they must be correctly located in the channel and, where appropriate, grouted in.

To ensure that the bond of the dovetail is not adversely affected, the shutters should not be stripped until the concrete has reached an adequate strength.

Cast-in sockets are used to provide threaded fixings in concrete panels. Unlike cast-in channels, they do not provide adjustment for positioning and their selection and installation must reflect this. Despite this, they are a means of providing an economic single point fixing. If adjustment is available elsewhere the lack of tolerance may not be important. Examples of their use are shown in Figures 3.6 and 3.7.

The sockets referred to in this guide should only be used for securing the cladding to the structure. Sockets used for lifting and transporting precast concrete are a different design and are covered elsewhere.

6.3 SUPERVISION

The quality of supervision is vital to achieving satisfactory long-term performance of the fixings and cladding system.

Problems related to tolerance commonly arise at the interfaces between different elements of the building envelope. They can arise from lack of early consultation between the parties involved, inadequate provision of tolerances in the design or poor workmanship. Reference should be made to the guidance in Sections 6.1.1 and 6.1.2.

Interfaces and buildability are being addressed by a DETR research project entitled *Structural frame and cladding buildability assessment method*, due to be completed in 2000. This will provide guidance to all those involved with the design, specification, manufacture, construction and erection of cladding systems and the structural frames supporting them, in order to minimise the problems that frequently occur as a result of inappropriately specified tolerances and/or incorrect or inaccurate installation.

To minimise potential problems of fit, the primary structure must be erected correctly to the tolerances specified. This should be checked by the cladding contractor, prior to the lines and levels of the cladding being set out as defined in the specification, to ensure the cladding can be erected in the correct positions using the specified fixing assemblies. Installation details must be clear and concise and detailed drawings are recommended. They must contain sufficient information to enable the correct installation procedure to be completed using the specified components.

All fixing components should be checked on delivery to the site for number, type and conformity to specification. All required tools must also be available on time. These would include an appropriate drilling machine, sufficient new drill bits of the required diameter and depth, hole-cleaning equipment (correct diameter brush and blowing device) and calibrated torque spanner of the correct range for torque-controlled anchors.

The fixers/installer should be experienced in installing the particular product. The engineer responsible on site must ensure that they are properly briefed and fully understand the requirements of the particular contract.

The installation process can be divided into stages. The correct execution of each stage is vital to the good functioning of the fixing assembly and cladding system, so supervision should ensure that each is properly undertaken and checked, and any errors are rectified as soon as possible. The critical stages of the installation are:

- location of cast-in fixings prior to casting operation
- location of holes for post-drilled fixings prior to drilling
- diameter and depth of holes prior to the insertion of fixings
- in the case of bonded fixings, the shelf life of resins and grouts should not be exceeded
- mixing technique for some bonded fixings and temperature at the time of installation: manufacturer's instructions must be followed
- curing time for bonded injection anchors
- installation torque in the case of torque controlled anchors.

If there are any problems that might result in deviation from the specified installation procedure, the designer should be notified and should approve the alternative fixing arrangement. All "as-built" alterations to the designed fixing detail should be marked on a master set of the clients' retained drawings.

Inspections of all fixings, after installation and before they are concealed behind cladding, should ensure that:

- the correct fixing system has been installed in accordance with the manufacturer's written instructions
- a suitable washer has been used, allowing adequate load distribution from the nut to the angle, bracket or cramp (eg plate washers are required over slotted holes)
- the maximum packing thickness has not been exceeded
- the bolts have been correctly tightened to the specified installation torque, using a calibrated torque spanner.

A checklist for supervisors is given in Appendix A.

Figure 6.9 shows an example of inadequate supervision, whereby the neopreen washer has been wrongly placed between the washer and the cramp. The correct position should be between the cramp and bracket, to minimise the corrosion between galvanised and stainless steel components.

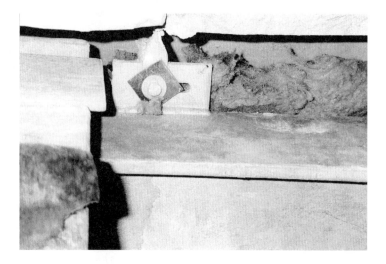

Figure 6.9   *An example of poor workmanship and inadequate supervision*

6.4   TESTING

6.4.1   Laboratory testing

When an approved fixing system is installed and used in accordance with the manufacturer's instructions, adhering to all spacing and distance recommendations and with adequate supervision, there is generally no need for additional testing. However this is frequently not the case so, more often than not, some testing is required.

It is the manufacturer's responsibility to select an appropriate test programme and provide the fixings performance data for the intended application.

Fixing products can be tested in accordance with a specific test method and then subsequently approved by an independent approval body. Such testing and approval is most commonly undertaken in the country of origin (eg the British Board of Agrément is the UK approval body). The reality is that to compete with the products in other countries, fixing manufacturers have to submit test data and the relevant analysis to the recognised approval bodies of those countries, in addition to gaining home country approval. This is an expensive and unnecessary exercise, particularly if the fixings have been subjected to the same testing regime as those already approved in the country.

This has been recognised and procedures are being introduced whereby approval by one EC country approval will automatically be accepted in any other European country. To date, a document covering fixings installed in concrete has been finalised and issued by European Organisation for Technical Approvals (EOTA), *Guideline for European Technical Approval (ETAG) for metal anchors for use in concrete*. This document sets out the requirements for post-drilled anchors, the acceptance criteria they have to meet, and the assessment and test methods used. It covers torque-controlled expansion anchors, undercut anchors, deformation-controlled expansion anchors and bonded injection anchors.

This document, even in draft format, has been extensively used over the past few years for testing fixings by a number of fixing manufacturers and independent testing laboratories. It is the most comprehensive document of this type. The test regimes are onerous and comprehensive in determining two key aspects of fixings performance: suitability and admissible service conditions.

The objectives for the tests are as follows:

- for suitability, the tests assess the susceptibility of the fixings to reasonable deviations from the installation procedure: eg oversized and undersized hole, fixing in contact with reinforcement, functioning with repeated loads etc

- for admissible service conditions, the tests determine the characteristic loads in relation to the condition of the base material (cracked or uncracked concrete), concrete strength, direction of loading, edge and spacing criteria etc.

There are already products on the market which have been developed to meet the onerous ETAG requirements, and selection of any of these products should give the specifier the maximum possible confidence.

The Construction Fixings Association has represented the UK fixings industry on the EOTA committee from its inception and has published a free Guidance Note: *European technical approvals for construction fixings*.

The British Standard for testing of fixings in concrete, natural stone, cast stone or brick or block masonry is BS 5080: *Structural fixings in concrete and masonry*. Part 1 covers methods of tests for tensile loading while Part 2 covers shear loading. The tests apply to the following types of anchors: expanding, bonded, cast-in channel inserts and undercut anchors. The tests can be undertaken for:

- comparative or reference purposes, for which a standard specimen of base material is fabricated in accordance with the mix prescribed by the document

- a specific application, in which case the base material may be either a specimen manufactured for the purpose or a representative section of the base material *in situ*.

BS 5080 is more conservative when setting out requirements for spacings, edge distances and clearances between test samples and the test rig than ETAG. The fundamental rule in establishing these distances is that in tests on single anchors without edge and spacing influences, the centre-to-centre distance and the distance from free edges must be sufficiently large to allow the formation of an unrestricted rupture cone with a vertex angel of 120°.

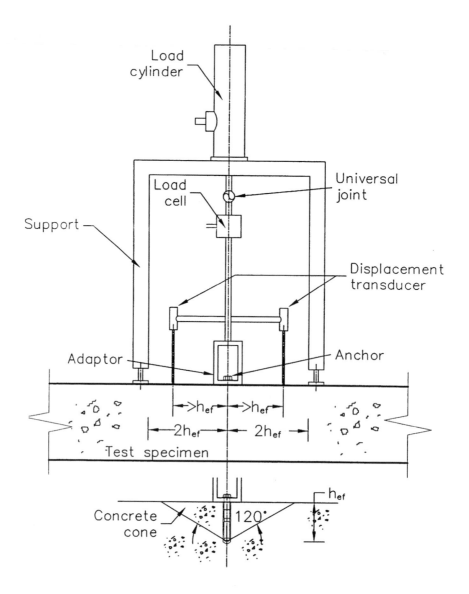

Figure 6.10   *Example of a tension test rig*

In all other aspects, BS 5080 and the ETAG 001 section on testing, *Annex A: Details of tests*, can be described as equivalent, but ETAG provides methods for a significantly larger number of tests, including oblique tests, sustained load tests, cyclic tests etc. The ETAG requirements regarding other aspects of testing (fixtures, monitoring etc) are also more detailed and up to date.

Although in its entirety the ETAG document refers to metal anchors installed in concrete, the test methods can be applied to all the products and base materials considered under BS 5080. It is therefore recommended that any laboratory testing is undertaken in accordance with ETAG 001 *Annex A: Details of tests*.

The selected test procedure must be based on the *in situ* loading conditions (tension, shear or the combination, ie oblique). If a test to failure is undertaken, it is not sufficient to establish failure loads only, but the load-displacement characteristics of the fixings must also be considered. Information on the acceptability of the load-displacement behaviour of different types of fixings can be found in a state-of-the-art report from the Comité Euro-International du Beton, *Fastenings to concrete and masonry structures.* This document compiles and compares the available experimental and theoretical research results concerning a large number of fixing systems.

It is, however, possible to present a simplified and idealised curve showing load-displacement characteristics applicable to any fixing system (see Figure 6.11).

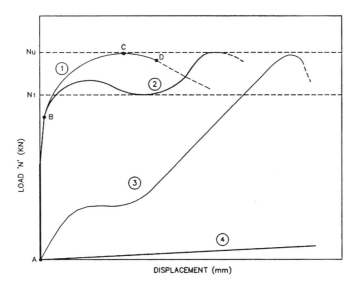

Figure 6.11   *Load-displacement curves*

Curve 1	*Idealised load displacement curve*
Curve 2	*Acceptable behaviour*
Curves 3 and 4	*Unacceptable behaviour*
A–B	*Initial fixity*
B	*First slip, generally taken as movement of 0.1 mm*
C	*Maximum load*
C–D	*Fixings in drilled holes only where load drops as friction or adhesion is overcome.*

The number of tests to be undertaken depends on several issues. If a specially prepared sample of the base material is manufactured, a balance should be struck between the confidence in the information gained and associated costs. The number of tests will generally vary between three and ten for a certain test type. Cost per test will generally reduce with the increased number of tests, while the confidence in results will increase with the increased number of tests. A minimum of five tests should be used for most purposes. Three tests can only give a very approximate guide to performance. If used to calculate characteristic loads, this will generally result in low values. An exception to this is if steel failure is expected or actually happens consistently. It is strongly recommended that no less than three tests of the same type be undertaken. Equally, undertaking more than ten tests of the same type would have a negligible effect on confidence increase in the results.

Although extremely rare, there are instances where there is a need for full prototype validation, eg if an existing product is intended for use outside the existing experience (close spacing and/or edge distances, innovative materials etc). In this case, a testing specification and acceptance criteria should be developed by the structural engineer, taking into considerations all factors that could potentially affect the performance of the fixing such as base material, worst scenario fixings configuration, worst loading conditions etc.

The Centre for Window and Cladding Technology is due to publish in 2000 a guidance document, *Strength of fixings for natural stone*, on the performance and testing of fixings for stone cladding, with particular emphasis on the fixing of thin stone panels.

6.4.2 Site testing

Site testing may be considered to satisfy the following objectives:

- to determine the suitability of a fixing for a specific application or admissible loads, especially where there is doubt about the nature or strength of the base material, a reasonable number of tests to failure will be necessary
- to check the quality of installation, proof tests can be carried out on a percentage of the total installation to a load sufficiently higher than the design load to ensure safety, but at the same time this load must not overload or damage correctly installed anchors.

BS 5080 was developed with laboratory testing in mind and does not address certain aspects of the practicalities of site testing or objectives, other than testing to failure for determining performance values. With this is mind, the Construction Fixings Association has published a Guidance Note, *Procedure for site testing construction fixings,* which seeks to complement BS 5080 in these areas. It relates closely to ETAG in certain areas.

Tests are usually carried out in tension to determine admissible tensile loads but, when performance in shear is particularly critical, shear tests can be carried out. Shear tests are more involved than tensile tests for two reasons: it is more complicated to transfer the externally applied test loads back to the structure and it is more demanding to measure the movement (usually the limiting factor for service loads).

Proof tests should not be carried out in shear as the quality of installation is indicated quite adequately by the performance in tension.

Test parameters

The following factors need careful consideration when carrying out site tests:

- number of tests
- location
- test equipment
- level of load (proof tests only)
- spacing of reaction loads
- monitoring movement
- test procedure
- reporting and assessment of results.

The above factors will now be briefly discussed, but the Construction Fixings Association Guidance Note gives further details.

Number of tests: For determination of allowable loads, at least five tests are recommended to give an adequate assessment of the consistency of results. There is little benefit from carrying out more than ten such tests. For proof loads to check installation quality, a percentage of at least 2.5 per cent (and at least three tests) should be checked. For safety-critical applications, especially on large projects, the percentage may be set high initially, say 10 per cent for the first 25 per cent of the total volume, reducing to a minimum of 2.5 per cent if there are no failures.

Location: For tests to failure, the location should be chosen such that any resulting damage will not affect the integrity of the structure and that it can be reported. For proof tests, fixings should be chosen as far as possible at random throughout the building.

Level of loading: For proof tests, the applied load should be 1.25–1.5 times either the manufacturer's recommended load or the design (applied) load. Higher proof loads may sometimes be justified but should not exceed twice the manufacturer's recommended load, as this may induce unnecessary movement or risk taking the bolt material beyond its yield point.

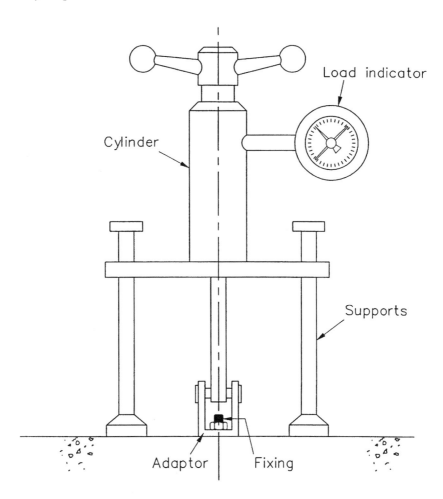

Figure 6.12   *A typical site test rig*

Spacing of reaction loads: Where tests to failure are required, the reaction loads should be directed into the base material beyond the zone of influence in order to allow a full cone failure to develop. For larger fixings, this may imply rigs that are too large to be practical on site. If smaller rigs are used, this should be noted in the report and the feet of any support should be as small as possible to minimise the potential interference with the cone. For proof tests, reduced spacing may be used, as cone failure is not expected (for normal proof load testing the reaction spacing is not critical, provided it is clear of the fixing). The Construction Fixings Association Guidance Note recommends suitable limits in relation to the magnitude of the proof load.

Monitoring movement: Movement does not necessarily need to be monitored in detail for either proof or failure tests in tension, but "first movement" should be noted to check that it occurs above the required design (applied) load, especially when the fixture is being clamped by the fixing, as is usually the case in cladding applications. It is generally not necessary to determine first movement too precisely and for most site tests a visual check is sufficient. Where first movement appears to be occurring before the applied or recommended load is achieved, more detailed monitoring using, for instance, a dial gauge, may be necessary. In this case, the responsible engineer should consider the displacement at the required service load in relation to the application.

6.4.3   Reporting

The reporting for both laboratory and site testing should contain the following:

- confirmation that tests have been carried out in accordance with a particular standard/document
- the name and location of the testing authority and the date of the tests
- the specification and description of the base material, including dimensions
- the description of the installation procedures
- the method of loading
- conformation of the dimensional requirements
- any modifications to the adopted test procedures
- the presentation of results. It is recommended that this is undertaken in accordance with BS 5080 which presents the results in graphical load-displacement form as well as in tabular form, summarising the ultimate loads for a particular test series. The presentation of the site test results is much simpler and can often be carried out in pass/fail format.

6.5   MAINTENANCE

6.5.1   Accessibility of fixings

Ideally the fixings should be accessible for inspection. This could be achieved by the use of demountable inner wall linings and it is also possible to view small cavities by means of fibre-optic probes. To undertake this, a small hole (approximately 15 mm diameter) is required to insert the probe and examine the condition of the fixing. It is also necessary that the location of all fixings be identified through the relevant documentation.

6.5.2 Concealed fixings

The reality is that most fixings are concealed and inaccessible. It is therefore particularly important that good practice is implemented in all stages from conception to installation to ensure their long-term performance. Concealed fixings will normally not need inspection during the life of the building but if an emergency necessitates inspections, a fibre-optic probe could be used.

Concealed fixings should not be assumed to be sealed and isolated. Water or acids etc may penetrate into the cavity and damage the fixings. Some cladding materials are cleaned using diluted hydrofluoric acid and, although the cladding offers some protection, water and cleaning chemicals may be forced into the cavity. Strong acid solutions should never be allowed to come into contact with any metal, including stainless steel. If this occurs, every attempt should be made to was it off immediately with generous amounts of water and specialist advice should be sought.

6.5.3 Exposed fixings

Occasionally some fixings are exposed for architectural reasons. Where fixings are accessible and rely on maintenance for their durability, this maintenance must be undertaken regularly.

The method of cleaning will often use water, which sometimes is applied under pressure. If exposed stainless-steel fixings and ancillary components are to maintain their appearance, they will require regular cleaning. The stainless steel can be cleaned with soap, detergent or a solution of ammonia, which may be used with a scrubbing brush. It should then be rinsed with clean water and wiped dry.

It is recommended that exposed architectural stainless-steel fixings are inspected for mechanical damage, surface contamination or incipient corrosion attack, at a frequency governed by the nature of the environment and the corrosion performance of the fixing materials. Where fixings made from less resistant material are exposed, regular inspections should be carried out to detect any defects which may affect their life expectancy.

6.5.4 Maintenance manual

The CDM Regulations require a health and safety file to be prepared and handed over to the client when the project is completed. This document should contain details of unusual features of the building which give rise to significant or unexpected health or safety hazards. In the context of cladding fixings, this could include:

- temporary support required when replacing fixings
- any particular order in which the cladding panels should be dismantled
- any features built into the structure or building to aid the inspection, maintenance or replacement of components of the cladding system (including its fixings).

This manual should contain all information necessary for inspection, maintenance and cleaning of fixings if required, ie type, location, etc. It should define maximum periods between these events.

The inspection and maintenance of exposed fixings should be undertaken when scaffolding is erected for the maintenance of the whole building. It must be undertaken by specialists. The frequency specified will depend on the nature of the cladding materials, fixings and the environment and varies significantly in practice. NFRC guidance for roofing and cladding recommends inspection every year.

Appendix A

A.1   CHECKLIST FOR FIXINGS DESIGNERS AND SPECIFIERS

ITEM	DESCRIPTION	COMMENT
1	Obtain full architectural and structural drawings with dead and live loading assumptions and environmental exposure details.	
2	Determine the nature of the supporting structure including movement.	
3	Agree loadings to be carried by the fixings with structural engineer and cladding manufacturer.	
4	Establish the available tolerances and methods of adjustment.	
5	Consult manufacturer's literature and select spacing, edge distance and embedment depth accordingly.	
6	Consider all health and safety issues regarding installation, use and removal of the fixings (include COSHH data sheets).	
7	Ideally involve the fixing and cladding installers and fixing manufacturers during design stages to incorporate their buildability expertise.	
8	Agree and carry out tests on sample cladding panels before work starts on installation.	
9	Provide the full reference for cladding fixings in specification and on drawings.	
10	Put all the required installation details on the drawings.	
11	Ensure that all maintenance information is passed to the building owner and occupier in the building's health and safety file.	

A.2   **CHECKLIST FOR SUPERVISOR/FOREMAN**

ITEM	DESCRIPTION	COMMENT
1	Ensure that current (latest revision) drawings are given to the installers and all superseded drawings are removed.	
2	Carry out a line and level survey of the structure to ensure fixings will still be within the acceptable tolerance range.	
3	Check as soon as possible with other contractors to avoid potential clashes between fixings and other building components.	
4	Check that the means of access for installation will allow a safe method of working. Ensure all other safety requirements are met, eg COSHH data sheets.	
5	Ensure that correct fixings are issued to the installers.	
6	Ensure that correct size, shape, material and total thickness of packing shims are used.	
7	Ensure that washers are correctly used with the fixings.	
8	Ensure that all installers are suitably experienced and qualified, and provide training appropriate to the project.	
9	Fully brief the site installation team and supervise sample panel trials.	
10	Supervise installation and notify designer of successes or problems with the fixing details.	
11	No modification is made to fixings, unless approved by designers.	

A.3 CHECKLIST FOR OPERATIVES INSTALLING FIXINGS

ITEM	DESCRIPTION	COMMENT
1	Have drawings that show the cladding components and fixings and their location.	
2	Review details and resolve problems before starting on the installation.	
3	Carry out sample panel installation to see how the fixing system works in practice.	
4	Ideally involve the installers during design stages to incorporate their buildability expertise (see Appendix A.1 for designers' checklist).	
5	Check that all the correct tools are available for installation.	
6	Check that the fixings issued from storage are those shown on the drawing before starting.	
7	Agree and check the method of access with the supervisor/foreman.	
8	Ensure harness connection points are provided, where this is a requirement of the installation method.	
9	Agree line and level datum points with supervisor before starting installation.	
10	If there are any doubts during installation regarding the eventual fixing system performance, advise the supervisor.	

A.4   **CHECKLIST FOR SITE TESTING**

ITEM	DESCRIPTION	COMMENT
1	Identify number of tests and location of each sample. This is normally defined in the project specification by the architect.	
2	Provide a method statement which will define the following information: • load(s) to be applied • manner in which it is applied (continuous or incremental, if incremental specify increments) • are loads to be maintained for a period of time at any level • establish whether it is necessary to monitor the movement and critical level of movement. This should ideally be approved by the architect.	
3	Identify pass and fail criteria.	
4	Check that all measuring equipment is calibrated traceably to National Standard. NAMAS Calibration Certificate for all measuring equipment must be available for inspection. The certificates must include measuring uncertainties (eg x kN for load cells, x mm for displacement transducers if used). If dropped, measuring equipment should be rechecked.	
5	Allocate a unique reference number to each sample and reference this back to the drawing.	
6	Provide pro forma result sheets.	
7	Identify independent source of testing if necessary. If failure of fixings can result in significant safety implications, tests must be either undertaken or witnessed by a suitably qualified body.	
8	Present test results in a clear and concise manner and ensure they are safely kept for future references.	

A.5   **CHECKLIST FOR LABORATORY TESTING**

ITEM	DESCRIPTION	COMMENT
1	Provide a method statement for testing. The method statement should define adopted test procedure with reference to the relevant standard. The following information must be clear from the method statement: • base material • installation procedure including spacings and edge distances • number of tests.	
2	Laboratory undertaking the testing should be NAMAS-accredited, with testing of fixings on the NAMAS-accredited list.	
3	If the laboratory undertaking the tests is not NAMAS-accredited, check that all measuring equipment is calibrated traceably to National Standards. NAMAS Calibration Certificates for all measuring equipment must be available for inspection. This information must include measuring uncertainties (eg x kN for load cells, x mm for displacement transducers if used).	
4	The load should ideally be applied in a continuous manner and if load to failure is applied the test should last in excess of 100 seconds. Displacements should be measured.	
5	Test results should be presented in tabular and graphical format.	

Appendix   B

B.1   QUESTIONNAIRE

Completed by: ....   Company name: ....

Position in company: ....   Contact telephone number: ....

1)   Are you a: Please tick

        a)   Consultant   ☐

        b)   Manufacturer   ☐

        c)   Designer   ☐

        d)   Supplier / distributor   ☐

        e)   Other – describe ....

2)   Is any aspect of your business related to the fixing of cladding?   Yes / No
    If 'yes' which type of cladding and in what proportion:

                                                           Proportion (%)

        a)   Curtain walling   ☐

        b)   Sheet metal   ☐

        c)   Precast concrete   ☐

        d)   Stone   ☐

        e)   Brickwork   ☐

3)   Are you aware of any examples of bad practice which might result in or may have had serious
    cladding fixings safety implications? If so, are you able to describe them and could you
    provide photographic examples?
    ....
    ....
    ....
    ....

4)   Do you believe that the current practices, including national standards and guidance
    documents, ensure safe performance of cladding fixings? Yes/No
    Please comment: ....
    ....
    ....
    ....

5)   Based on your knowledge and experience what is your view on how awareness of good
    practice can be increased?
    ....
    ....
    ....
    ....

Please continue on separate sheet if required

Item	COMPANY TYPE	Business Activities					EXAMPLES OF BAD PRACTICE?	SAFE PERFORMANCE?	HOW CAN GOOD PRACTICE BE INCREASED?
		CW	SM	PC	S	B			
1	Manufacturer	10%	10%				Not aware of any.	No. Blind fixing using tape/adhesive.	Better understanding between structural engineers and adhesive manufacturers.
2	Manufacturer/designer			5%	75%	20%	Anchor bolts not installed/torqued properly. Insulation washers omitted. Inadequate details supplied to installer.	No standard can ensure safe performance but with adequate QC measures it can be implemented correctly.	Adequate training and quality control measures.
3	Consultant	20%	20%	20%	20%	20%	Fixing brackets omitted. Inadequate brackets with excessive packing. Poor quality of brackets and poor fixing of them.	Problems tend to occur on smaller projects because there is no guidance/supervision of the installer.	Using a simple, clearly illustrated guide.
4	Supplier/distributor						No comment made.	Inadequate ventilation to and weatherproofing of fixings.	Using publications and through rules and legislation.
5	Consultant/supplier	50%	40%	8%	1%	1%	Refer to case studies in Dr Bruoke's thesis.	Standards are seen as a means of specification control only.	Better training.
6	Consultant	2%	1%	1%	1%	10%	Effect of incompatible tolerances not understood - often results in fixing being packed out excessively or spanning a greater gap than designed for.	Insufficient attention paid to checking what has been achieved, rather than design intended. Many fixings cannot be regularly inspected once facade is complete.	Installers should carry a card stating their competencies. Critical connections should only be undertaken by appropriately qualified staff.
7	Manufacturer					5%	No.	Yes.	Update reference documents.
8	Supplier/distributor							Not relevant to its business.	
9	Manufacturer	10%	60%	10%	10%	10%	Using temporary fasteners for lining out whole roof. Using imported fasteners designed for different purlin thicknesses. Installation using incorrect tools. Not considering bi-metal interaction when selecting a fastener.	BS 5427 is out of date. NFRC guide is biased due to marketing influence of contributors.	By hallmarking products and installers as proposed by the Roofing Alliance. Using an independent guide free from commercial influences.
10	Manufacturer		100%				Not aware of any.	Yes.	By using reputable suppliers and following their technical advice.
11	Manufacturer							Not relevant to its business.	
12	Manufacturer							Not relevant to its business.	
13	Manufacturer/designer	33%		33%		34%	Unsuitable design method. Wrong fixing specification. Unsuitable fixing type. Installation error.	Currently in the legislation, there is no mention of the latest fixing method - stress-free undercut anchors.	To achieve a greater understanding of the latest state-of-the-art cladding technology. Legislation.
14	Designer	1%	1%	1%			Do not have the experience to comment.	Installers use the cheapest type of fixing. Standards should be set to ensure only BS-rated fixings are used.	Ensure BS-rated fixings are used.
15	Manufacturer			33%	33%	34%	No. Has improved considerably since 1960s.	Yes. See BS 8298 and BS 5628.	Training at operative level.

Item	COMPANY TYPE	Business Activities					EXAMPLES OF BAD PRACTICE?	SAFE PERFORMANCE?	HOW CAN GOOD PRACTICE BE INCREASED?
		CW	SM	PC	S	B			
16	Manufacturer/designer/							Not relevant to its business.	
17	Manufacturer/designer/ supplier	25%		25%	25%	25%	Insufficient bearing on brick support systems. Inadequate shimming behind support brackets and too many shims.	Site supervision seems to be the main problem.	Training. Introduction of a guide with good practices to be adhered to.
18	Manufacturer/designer							Not relevant to its business.	
19	Manufacturer							Not relevant to its business.	
20	Designer							Not relevant to its business.	
21	Supplier/distributor	15%	75%			10%	On many of the smaller contracts fixers ignore the rules as this would slow down completion of the contract.	Yes.	Greater supervision.
22	Designer						No.	Greater emphasis on correct selection and installation of fixings.	Greater supervision.
23	Designer							Not relevant to its business.	
24	Contractor				70%		Refer to Peter Harrison's information.	No comment made.	Training.
25	Manufacturer							Not relevant to its business.	
26	Manufacturer/designer/ supplier	1%		2%	10%	87%	Stonework restraints - insufficient projection into the cladding/ incorrect material used (ie stainless steel not used).	Yes. Except for sometimes contradicting/confusing information between DD140, BS 1243, BS 5628 and Building Regulations.	Better integration of standards/statutory documents.

231 questionnaires sent out
26 replies received
9 replies not relevant

CW	Curtain Walling
SM	Sheet Metal
PC	Precast Concrete
S	Stone
B	Brickwork

Sources of information

ALUMINIUM FEDERATION
Broadway House
Calthorpe Road
Five Ways
Edgbaston
Birmingham B15 1TN
Tel: 0121 456 1103

BRICK DEVELOPMENT ASSOCIATION
Woodside House
Winkfield
Windsor
Berkshire SL4 2DX
Tel: 01344 885 651

BRITISH BOARD OF AGRÉMENT
PO Box No 195
Bucknalls Lane
Garston
Watford
Hertfordshire WD2 7NG
Tel: 01923 670 844

CENTRE FOR WINDOW AND CLADDING TECHNOLOGY
University of Bath
Claverton Road
Bath BA2 7AY
Tel: 01225 826 541

CONSTRUCTION FIXINGS ASSOCIATION
Light Trades House
3 Melbourne Avenue
Sheffield S10 2QJ
Tel: 0114 266 3084

COPPER DEVELOPMENT ASSOCIATION
Verulam Industrial Estate
224 London Road
St Albans
Hertfordshire AL1 1AQ
Tel: 01727 731 200

COUNCIL FOR ALUMINIUM IN BUILDING
191 Cirencester Road
Charlton Kings
Cheltenham
Gloucestershire GL53 8DF
Tel: 01242 578 278

METAL CLADDING AND ROOFING MANUFACTURERS ASSOCIATION
18 Mere Farm Road
Noctorum
Birkenhead
Merseyside L43 9TT
Tel: 0151 652 3846

NATIONAL FEDERATION OF ROOFING CONTRACTORS
24 Weymouth Street
London W1N 4IX
Tel: 020 7436 0387

NICKEL DEVELOPMENT INSTITUTE
The Holloway
Alvechurch
Birmingham B48 7QB
Tel: 01527 584 777

STEEL CONSTRUCTION INSTITUTE
Silwood Park
Ascot
Berkshire SL5 7QN
Tel: 01344 623 345

References

THE BRICK DEVELOPMENT ASSOCIATION AND
BRITISH STEEL CORPORATION (1986)
Brick cladding to steel framed buildings
Publication BDA DG 18

BRITISH RESEARCH ESTABLISHMENT (1980)
Fixings for non-load-bearing precast concrete panels
Digest 235

BRITISH RESEARCH ESTABLISHMENT (1990)
Corrosion of steel wall ties
Information Papers IP 12/90 & 13/90

BRITISH STANDARDS INSTITUTION (1991)
Specification for wrought steels for mechanical and allied engineering purposes
BS 970: BSI, London

BRITISH STANDARDS INSTITUTION (1997)
Specification for cast stone
BS 1217: BSI, London

BRITISH STANDARDS INSTITUTION (1978)
Metal ties for cavity wall construction
BS 1243: BSI, London

BRITISH STANDARDS INSTITUTION (1991)
Parts 1.2 and 1.5 – steel plate, sheet and strip
Part 2:1983 (1991) – specification for stainless and heat resisting plate, sheet and strip
BS 1449: BSI, London

BRITISH STANDARDS INSTITUTION
Steel wire for cold forged fasteners for similar components
Part 1:1987 - specification for carbon and low alloy steel wire
Part 2:1979 - stainless steel
BS 3111: BSI, London

BRITISH STANDARDS INSTITUTION (1997)
Specification for carbon steel bars for the reinforcement of concrete
BS 4449: BSI, London

BRITISH STANDARDS INSTITUTION
Structural fixings in concrete and masonry
Part 1:1993 – method of test for tensile loading
Part 2: 1986 – method for determination of resistance to lading in shear
BS 5080: BSI, London

BRITISH STANDARDS INSTITUTION (1976)
Code of practice for stone masonry
BS 5390: BSI, London

BRITISH STANDARDS INSTITUTION (1976)
Code of practice for performance and loading criteria for profiled sheeting in building
Part 1: 1996 – Code of practice for the use of profiled sheet for roof and wall cladding
on buildings
BS 5427: BSI, London

BRITISH STANDARDS INSTITUTION (1990)
Code of practice for accuracy in building
BS 5606: BSI, London

BRITISH STANDARDS INSTITUTION (1985)
Use of masonry
Part 1: 1992 – *Structural use of unreinforced masonry*
Part 3: 1985 – *Materials and components, design and workmanship*
BS 5628: BSI, London

BRITISH STANDARDS INSTITUTION (1981)
Specification for corrosion resistant stainless steel fasteners
BS 6105: BSI, London

BRITISH STANDARDS INSTITUTION (1997)
Loading for buildings
Part 2 - Code of practice for wind loads
BS 6399: BSI, London

BRITISH STANDARDS INSTITUTION (1986)
Specification for austenitic stainless steel bars for the reinforcement of concrete
BS 6744: BSI, London

BRITISH STANDARDS INSTITUTION (1991)
Coatings on metal fasteners
BS 7371: BSI, London

BRITISH STANDARDS INSTITUTION (1992)
Guide to durability of buildings and building elements, products and components
BS 7543: BSI, London

BRITISH STANDARDS INSTITUTION (1995)
Code of practice for design and installation of non-load-bearing precast
concrete cladding
BS 8297: BSI, London

BRITISH STANDARDS INSTITUTION (1994)
Code of practice for design and installation of natural stone cladding and lining
BS 8298: BSI, London

BRITISH STANDARDS ISTITUTION (1998)
Mechanical properties of corrosion-resistant stainless steel fasteners
BS EN ISO 3506-1: BSI, London

BRITISH STANDARDS INSTITUTION (1993)
Hot rolled products of non-alloy structural steels, technical delivery conditions
BS EN 10025: BSI, London

BRITISH STANDARDS INSTITUTION (1995)
Stainless steels
Part 1:1995 – list of stainless steels
Part 2:1995 – technical delivery conditions for sheet/plate and strip for
general purposes
Part 3:1995 – technical delivery conditions for semi-finished products,
bars, rods and sections for general purposes
BS EN 10088: BSI, London

BRITISH STANDARDS INSTITUTION (1992)
Mechanical properties of fasteners
Part 1:1992 – Bolts, screws and studs
BS EN 20898: BSI, London

BRITISH STANDARDS INSTITUTION (1987)
Wall ties
DD140: Part 2 – *Recommendations for design of wall tiles*

BRITISH STANDARDS INSTITUTION (1979)
Commentary on corrosion at bimetallic contacts and its alleviation
PD 6484: BSI, London

BRITISH STEEL (1988)
Roofing and cladding in steel – a guide to architectural practice

CENTRE FOR WINDOW AND CLADDING TECHNOLOGY (1997)
Performance and testing of fixings for thin stone cladding
Guidance document

CENTRE FOR WINDOW AND CLADDING TECHNOLOGY (1997)
Guide to the selection and testing of stone panels for external use

CIRIA (2000)
The use of epoxy, polyester and similar reactive polymers in construction.
Volume 1: The materials and their practical applications
C537

CIRIA (1997)
CDM Regulations - work sector guidance for designers
Report 166

CIRIA (1990)
Fixings in cracked concrete: the probability of coincident occurrence and
likely crack width
Technical Note 136

CIRIA (1991)
Selection and use of fixings in concrete and masonry: interim update to CIRIA Guide 4
Technical Note 137

CIRIA (1983)
A suggested design procedure for accuracy in building
Technical Note 113

CIRIA (1992)
Wall technology: Volumes A to G
Special Publication 87

CIRIA (1998)
Sealant joints in the external envelope of buildings: a guide to design, specification and construction
Report 178

COMITÉ EURO-INTERNATIONAL DU BETON (1994)
Fastenings to concrete and masonry structures
State-of-the-art Report, Thomas Telford Services Ltd, 1994

COMITÉ EURO-INTERNATIONAL DU BETON (1995)
Design of fastenings in concrete
Design guide, Thomas Telford Services Ltd, 1997

COMITÉ EURO-INTERNATIONAL DU BETON (1995)
Fastenings for seismic retrofitting
State-of-the-art Report, Thomas Telford Services Ltd, 1997

THE CONCRETE SOCIETY (1998)
Guidance on the use of stainless steel reinforcement
Technical Report 51

CONSTRUCTION (DESIGN AND MANAGEMENT) REGULATIONS (1994)

CONSTRUCTION FIXINGS ASSOCIATION – GUIDANCE DOCUMENTS
Anchor selection (1995)
Anchor installation (1996)
Procedure for site testing construction fixings (1994)
Introduction to bonded anchors (1994)
Heavy duty expansion anchors (1997)
Fixings for brickwork and blockwork (1997)
Fixings and fire (1998)
European technical approvals for construction fixings (1998)
Undercut anchors (1999)

DEPARTMENT OF THE ENVIRONMENT AND WELSH OFFICE (1992)
A1 Loading in *Building Regulations 1991, Approved document A – Structures*

EUROPEAN ORGANISATION FOR TECHNICAL APPROVALS (1997)
ETAG 001 Guideline for European Technical Approvals of metal anchors for use in concrete

INSTITUTION OF CIVIL ENGINEERS (1993)
Appraisal and repair of cladding and fixings

INSTITUTION OF STRUCTURAL ENGINEERS (1995)
Aspects of cladding

NICKEL DEVELOPMENT INSTITUTE (1995)
Stainless steel in swimming pool buildings, a guide to selection and use

THE NATIONAL FEDERATION OF ROOFING CONTRACTORS (1991)
Profiled sheet metal roofing and cladding, a guide to good practice

STEEL CONSTRUCTION INSTITUTE (1996)
Curtain wall connections to steel frames
SCI P101

STEEL CONSTRUCTION INSTITUTE (1996)
Connections between steel and other materials
SCI P102

STEEL CONSTRUCTION INSTITUTE (1993)
Design of stainless steel fixings and ancillary components
SCI P119

STEEL CONSTRUCTION INSTITUTE (1993)
Concise guide to the structural design of stainless steel
SCI P123

STEEL CONSTRUCTION INSTITUTE (1995)
Stainless steel angles for masonry support
SCI P157

STEEL CONSTRUCTION INSTITUTE (1996)
Architects guide to stainless steel
SCI P179

UK GALVANISERS' ASSOCIATION (1989)
Steelwork protection guide